CLASSROOM ACTIVITY BOOK

D1358683

Contents

ESTIMATION—GRADE 2

MENTAL MATH—GRADE 2

CONSUMER—GRADE 2

Pupil Edition Chapter	Teacher Instruction Page	Student Page
Chapter 1	—	1
Chapter 2	—	2
Chapter 3	—	3
Chapter 4	—	4
Chapter 5	—	5
Chapter 6	—	6
Chapter 7	—	7
Chapter 8	—	8
Chapter 9	—	9
Chapter 10	—	10
Chapter 11	—	11
Chapter 12	—	12

CALCULATOR—GRADE 2

Pupil Edition Chapter	Teacher Instruction Page	Student Page
Chapter 1	—	1, 2
Chapter 2	—	3, 4
Chapter 3	—	5, 6
Chapter 4	—	7, 8
Chapter 5	—	9, 10
Chapter 6	—	11, 12
Chapter 7	—	13, 14
Chapter 8	—	15, 16
Chapter 9	—	17, 18
Chapter 10	—	19, 20
Chapter 11	—	21, 22
Chapter 12	—	23, 24

COMPUTER—GRADE 2

Pupil Edition Chapter	Teacher Instruction Page	Student Page
Chapter 1	—	1
Chapter 2	—	2
Chapter 3	—	3
Chapter 4	—	4
Chapter 5	—	5
Chapter 6	—	6
Chapter 7	—	7
Chapter 8	—	8
Chapter 9	—	9
Chapter 10	—	10
Chapter 11	—	11
Chapter 12	—	12

LISTENING AND WRITING MATH—GRADE 2

Pupil Edition Chapter	Teacher Instruction Page	Student Page
Chapter 1	T1	—
Chapter 2	T2, T3, T4	1, 2, —
Chapter 3	T1, T5	—, 3
Chapter 4	T1, T6	—, 4
Chapter 5	T1	—
Chapter 6	T1, T7, T8, T9, T10	—, 5, 6, 7, 8
Chapter 7	T1, T11	—, 9
Chapter 8	T12	—
Chapter 9	T13	10
Chapter 10	T14	11
Chapter 11	T12, T15	—, 12, 13, 14, 15
Chapter 12	T12, T16	—, 16

MATH RELAYS—GRADE 2

FAMILY INVOLVEMENT—GRADE 2

ESTIMATION   Weight

Mark the one that goes on the other end of
the seesaw.

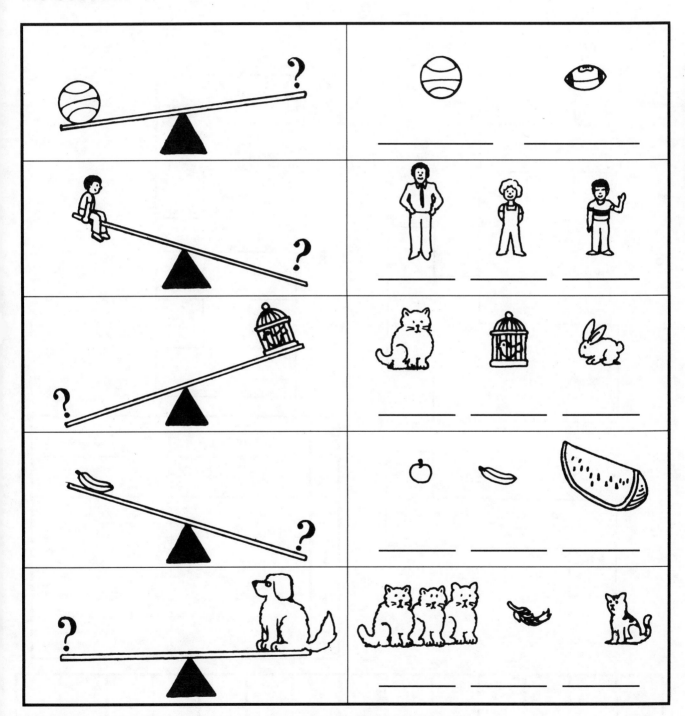

Children mark the object that will keep the seesaw in the positions shown.

ESTIMATION   Area

Cut out the squares along the dotted line.
Guess how many squares will cover each
space. Check using the squares.

1.

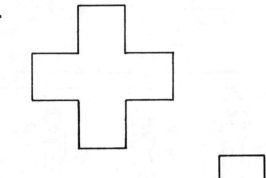

2.

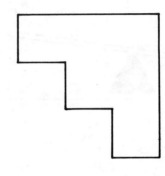

3.

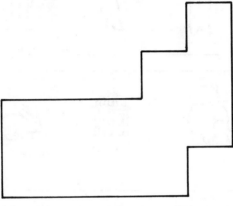

4.

5.

	Guess	Check
1.		
2.		
3.		
4.		
5.		

ESTIMATION   **Capacity**

One bottle will fill 4 glasses.

Ring either *yes* or *no*.

1. Will 🍶 fill 🥛 🥛 🥛 🥛 🥛 ?   yes   no

2. Will 🍶🍶 fill 🥛 🥛 🥛 🥛 🥛 ?   yes   no

3. Will 🍶🍶 fill 🥛🥛🥛🥛🥛🥛🥛 ?   yes   no

4. Will 🍶 fill 🥛 🥛 🥛 🥛 🥛 🥛 ?   yes   no

5. Will 🍶🍶🍶 fill 🥛🥛🥛🥛 ?   yes   no

ESTIMATION   **Number Sense**

1	2	3	4	5	6	7	8	9	10
11	12	13	14	15	16	17	18	19	20
21	22	23	24	25	26	27	28	29	30
31	32	33	34	35	36	37	38	39	40
41	42	43	44	45	46	47	48	49	50
51	52	53	54	55	56	57	58	59	60
61	62	63	64	65	66	67	68	69	70
71	72	73	74	75	76	77	78	79	80
81	82	83	84	85	86	87	88	89	90
91	92	93	94	95	96	97	98	99	

Write your guess in the Guess column. Check
your answer by counting.

Write how many numbers	Guess	Check
1. start with a 6.		
2. end with a 5.		
3. have an 8.		
4. have the same number twice.		
5. are less than 15.		
6. are less than 30 but more than 20.		

Name _____ Date _____

Write your guess in the Guess column. Then check your answers. How many times in 10 seconds can you

	Guess	Check
1. clap your hands?	_____	_____
2. hop up and down?	_____	_____
3. snap your fingers?	_____	_____
4. touch your toes?	_____	_____

How many times in 20 seconds can you

	Guess	Check
5. touch your nose?	_____	_____
6. touch your toes?	_____	_____
7. snap your fingers?	_____	_____
8. walk to the blackboard?	_____	_____

Do you think that Maria can

9. snap her fingers 75 times in 10 seconds?   yes   no

10. touch her toes 5 times in 10 seconds?   yes   no

11. hop 100 times in 15 seconds?   yes   no

12. clap her hands 80 times in 20 seconds?   yes   no

ESTIMATION   **Number Sense**

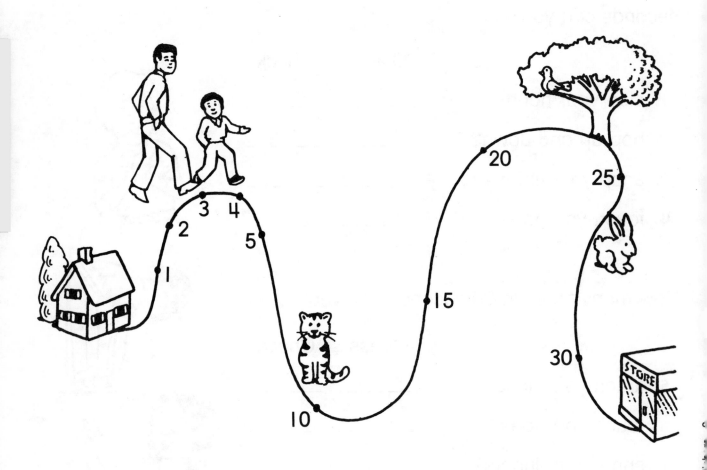

Use the number line shown to answer the question.

1. About what number is the cat on? _____

2. Name a number before the cat. _____

3. About what number is the store on? _____

4. About what number is the bird on? _____

5. About what number is the rabbit on? _____

ESTIMATION   **Number Sense**

Guess. Then count.

1. How many circles are there?

   Guess _____   Count _____

   How many groups of ⭕ are there? _____

2. How many squares are there?

   Guess _____   Count _____

   How many groups of ◻ are there? _____

ESTIMATION   Addition

Ring the addends that add to more than 10.

1. $8 + 2$

2. $0 + 7$

3. $3 + 9$

4. $3 + 8$

5. $6 + 8$

6. $7 + 7$

7. $3 + 5$

8. $1 + 3$

9. $2 + 4$

10. $8 + 4$

11. $9 + 4$

12. $8 + 7$

13. $6 + 7$

14. $4 + 3$

15. $0 + 8$

16. $9 + 6$

17. $6 + 5$

18. $9 + 2$

19. How many sums are greater than 10?

fewer than 5 _____

between 5 and 10 _____

more than 10 _____

ESTIMATION   **Measurement**

Cut out the candles along the dotted lines.
Guess how many candles tall each object is.
Measure to check.

Number of candles tall		
	Guess	Check
Fork		
Brush		
Pen		
Can		

ESTIMATION   **Measurement**

Ring the best answer.

Could

		yes	no
1.	your bed be 2 meters long?	yes	no
2.	a traffic light be 3 meters high?	yes	no
3.	your uncle be 3 meters tall?	yes	no
4.	a mountain be 15 centimeters high?	yes	no
5.	a new pencil be 18 centimeters long?	yes	no
6.	a book be 2 meters thick?	yes	no
7.	a shoe be 27 centimeters long?	yes	no
8.	a baseball bat be 7 meters long?	yes	no
9.	a red crayon be 10 centimeters long?	yes	no
10.	a button be 1 meter wide?	yes	no

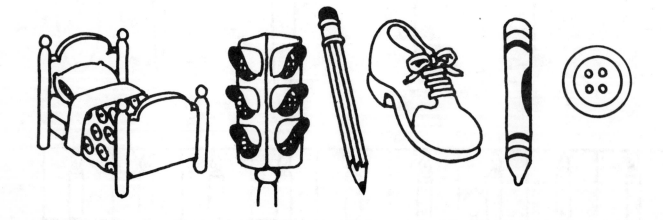

   Use after pages 129–130.

Name _____ Date _____

Ring the addends that add to more than 99.

1. 36 + 16

2. 29 + 68

3. 47 + 6

4. 55 + 12

5. 83 + 18

6. 17 + 81

7. 39 + 71

8. 49 + 46

9. 11 + 88

10. 75 + 19

11. 2 + 98

12. 61 + 39

13. How many sums are greater than 80?

fewer than 5 _____

between 5 and 10 _____

more than 10 _____

ESTIMATION Number Sense

Ring the number that does not belong.

1. 10   20
   30
   12   40

2. 18   28
   52
   38   48

3. 158   200
   400
   300   100

4. 2   5
   4
   6   8

5. 56   27
   23
   25   22

6. 66   65
   10
   36   26

7. 88   44
   77
   13   22

8. 5   10
   15
   20   8

9. 23   15
   17
   10   18

10. 8   42
    6
    2   5

11. 102   269
    478
    56   223

12. 98   87
    92
    85   21

ESTIMATION ANSWER KEY

Page 1

Row 1: football
Row 2: first figure
Row 3: cat
Row 4: watermelon
Row 5: three cats

Page 2

1. Answers will vary. 5
2. Answers will vary. 6
3. Answers will vary. 12
4. Answers will vary. 7
5. Answers will vary. 7

Page 3

1. no
2. yes
3. no
4. yes
5. yes

Page 4

Col. 1: Answers will vary.
1. 10
2. 10
3. 18
4. 9

Page 4 (cont'd.)

5. 14
6. 9

Page 5

1.–8. Answers will vary.
9. no
10. yes
11. no
12. yes

Page 6

1. 9
2. 1–8
3. 32
4. 24
5. 27

Page 7

1. Answers will vary; 52; 10
2. Answers will vary; 33; 6

Page 8

Ring addends in 3, 4, 5, 6, 10, 11, 12, 13, 16, 17, and 18. Check "more than 10."

Page 9

Guess Column: Answers will vary.
Check Column: 6
7
4
2

Page 10

1. yes
2. no
3. no
4. no
5. yes
6. no
7. yes
8. no
9. yes
10. no

Page 11

Ring addends in 5, 7, 11, and 12. Check "between 5 and 10."

Page 12

1. 12   2. 52   3. 158   4. 5   5. 56
6. 10   7. 13   8. 8   9. 23   10. 42
11. 56   12. 21

MENTAL MATH Teacher's Instructions

CHAPTER 1 Recognizing Complements of 10
Use after textbook pages 7–8.   page 1
Explain to children that each flower box can hold 10 flowers.
Children must determine how many more flowers can be added to fill
each box. Point out that the first box already has 9 flowers. Ask them
how many more flowers the box can hold. Do this exercise verbally
and repeat until children can quickly recognize the tens complement
of a 1-digit number.

CHAPTER 2 Counting Back by 1, 2, and 3
Use after textbook pages 49–50.   page 2
Give each child a hundreds chart. Show them that the chart can be
used to count back from a number. Ask them to ring 14 and then
count back 2. Have them put an X on this number, 12. Continue to
ask them to ring a number, count back 1, 2, or 3, and put an X on the
number. Have children practice counting back 1, 2, or 3 without the
hundreds chart.

CHAPTER 3 Counting On by 1, 2, and 3
Use after textbook pages 75–76.   page 3
Give each child a hundreds chart. Show them that the chart can be
used to count on from a number. Ask them to ring 16 and then count
on 3. Have them put an X on this number, 19. Continue to ask them to
ring a number, count on 1, 2, or 3, and put an X on the number. Have
children practice counting on 1, 2, or 3 without the hundreds chart.

CHAPTER 4 Addition and Subtraction to 18
Use after textbook pages 93–94.   page 4
Explain to children that solving subtraction problems is easier if you
think of addition. For example: $14 - 7 = ?$ Think: $7 + 7 = 14$; so, $14 - 7 = 7$. Give children other examples of fact families. $10 - 6 = ?$
Think: $6 + 4 = 10$; so, $10 - 6 = 4$. Have them complete the addition
problem for the first six problems. Children can say the addition
problems for the remaining problems softly as they solve.

CHAPTER 5 Before, After, and Between
Use after texbook pages 107–108.   page 5
Tell children that you have seen a film of the Great International Road
Race and that you know which car won. Give children clues that use
the words *before, after,* and *between.* For example, the cars
numbered between 31 and 39 did not finish first; the cars after 45 did
not finish first; the cars before 32 did not cross the finish line first;
the car before 41 came in last; the cars between 40 and 46 did not
finish first. Children should draw a line through each car that did not
finish first. They should ring the winning car (39). Give children a
fresh workbook page and repeat the exercise; have a different car
winning the race.

CHAPTER 6 Recognizing Complements of Multiples of 10
Use after textbook pages 161–162.   page 6
Explain to children that if they recognize numbers that add up to 10,
they can add large numbers in their heads. Have the children say the
sums of these problems verbally: $1 + 9$; $2 + 8$; $3 + 7$; $4 + 6$; $5 + 5$;
$6 + 4$; $7 + 3$; $8 + 2$; $9 + 1$. Then have them look at the sheet. If the
numbers in the ones place add up to 10, write a zero in the ones
place and add 1 more to the tens place to solve the problem. Tell
children to add mentally and then to draw a line to the correct
answer.

CHAPTER 7 Adding by Looking for Multiples of 10
Use after textbook pages 177–178.   page 7
Explain to children that looking for a group of ten can help them
solve addition problems. When adding 8 and 3, for example, children
should look for a group of ten by ringing the 8 marbles plus 2 of the
3 marbles. One marble is left. 10 + 1 = 11. When adding 18 and 3,
ring the group of ten marbles. Then ring the 8 marbles and 2 of the 3
marbles. 10 + 10 + 1 = 21. In the first two exercises, children
should practice ringing to make groups of ten marbles. For the rest
of the problems, children should continue to make groups of ten in
their heads.

CHAPTER 8 Subtracting a Number from a Multiple of 10
Use after textbook pages 195–196.   page 8
Go through the first nine exercises with children. Then ask them what
20 − 1 would equal. To help them figure it out, have them look at 10
− 1. Point out that 10 − 1 = 9. 20 − 1 = 19. 30 − 1 = 29. Then ask
children to complete the subtraction exercises by subtracting in their
heads. They can use the first group of exercises as a model.

CHAPTER 9 Adding by Looking for Multiples of 10
Use after texbook pages 233–234   page 9
Give each child a copy of the hundreds chart. Show how to add 13
and 10 on the chart. Ask children to put a finger on the number 13
and then count forward 1 row or 10 spaces to 23. Repeat this
procedure by using 13 + 20, 13 + 30, 13 + 40, and so on. Point out
that the sum of 13 + 20 is 33. The number 33 is 2 rows below the
number 13 on the chart. 13 + 30 = 43. The number 43 is 3 rows
below the number 13. Then read the following exercises using
addition of multiples of 10 to 2-digit numbers. Ask students to figure
out how many rows to move and ring the sum for each exercise.

1. 17 + 10 = <u>27</u>   **2.** 17 + 40 = <u>57</u>   **3.** 17 + 60 = <u>77</u>
4. 24 + 10 = <u>34</u>   **5.** 24 + 30 = <u>54</u>   **6.** 24 + 40 = <u>64</u>
7. 35 + 10 = <u>45</u>   **8.** 35 + 20 = <u>55</u>   **9.** 35 + 40 = <u>75</u>

Then point out to children that they can add multiples of 10 another
way. To add numbers like 53 and 30, first add the tens place. 5 tens
+ 3 tens = 8 tens, or 80. Then add the ones: 80 + 3 = 83. Practice
adding a multiple of 10 to a 2-digit number without using the
hundreds chart.

CHAPTER 10 Subtracting with Multiples of 10
Use after pages 279–280.   page 10
Explain to the children that it is faster to subtract mentally if they
subtract the tens place first and then the ones place. Tell the children
they can use a finger to cover the ones place as they subtract the
tens place. They can then cover the tens place with their finger as
they subtract the ones place.

CHAPTER 11 Adding 8 or 9 to a Number
Use after pages 313–314.   page 11
Explain to the children that it is easy to add 10 to a number. It is also
easy to add 8 or 9. To add 9, add 10 then subtract 1. To add 8, add 10
then subtract 2.

CHAPTER 12 Recognizing Compatible Numbers
Use after pages 339–340.   page 12
Have the children review the numbers with a sum of 10. Explain that
when adding or subtracting a chain of numbers, they should always
look ahead for pairs of numbers which make their calculations easier.

MENTAL MATH   Recognizing Complements of 10

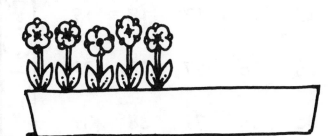

MENTAL MATH   Counting Back by 1, 2, and 3

0	1	2	3	4	5	6	7	8	9
10	11	12	13	14	15	16	17	18	19
20	21	22	23	24	25	26	27	28	29
30	31	32	33	34	35	36	37	38	39
40	41	42	43	44	45	46	47	48	49
50	51	52	53	54	55	56	57	58	59
60	61	62	63	64	65	66	67	68	69
70	71	72	73	74	75	76	77	78	79
80	81	82	83	84	85	86	87	88	89
90	91	92	93	94	95	96	97	98	99

MENTAL MATH | Counting On by 1, 2, and 3

0	1	2	3	4	5	6	7	8	9
10	11	12	13	14	15	16	17	18	19
20	21	22	23	24	25	26	27	28	29
30	31	32	33	34	35	36	37	38	39
40	41	42	43	44	45	46	47	48	49
50	51	52	53	54	55	56	57	58	59
60	61	62	63	64	65	66	67	68	69
70	71	72	73	74	75	76	77	78	79
80	81	82	83	84	85	86	87	88	89
90	91	92	93	94	95	96	97	98	99

MENTAL MATH   Addition and Subtraction to 18

Subtract mentally.

$7 +$ _____ $= 15$ $8 +$ _____ $= 16$

1. $15 - 7 =$ _____   2. $16 - 8 =$ _____

$9 +$ _____ $= 14$ $9 +$ _____ $= 17$

3. $14 - 9 =$ _____   4. $17 - 9 =$ _____

$6 +$ _____ $= 15$ $9 +$ _____ $= 18$

5. $15 - 6 =$ _____   6. $18 - 9 =$ _____

7.
$$\begin{array}{r} 14 \\ -\ 6 \\ \hline \end{array}$$

8.
$$\begin{array}{r} 16 \\ -\ 9 \\ \hline \end{array}$$

9.
$$\begin{array}{r} 10 \\ -\ 8 \\ \hline \end{array}$$

10.
$$\begin{array}{r} 14 \\ -\ 5 \\ \hline \end{array}$$

11.
$$\begin{array}{r} 16 \\ -\ 7 \\ \hline \end{array}$$

12.
$$\begin{array}{r} 15 \\ -\ 8 \\ \hline \end{array}$$

13.
$$\begin{array}{r} 12 \\ -\ 6 \\ \hline \end{array}$$

14.
$$\begin{array}{r} 13 \\ -\ 8 \\ \hline \end{array}$$

MENTAL MATH   Before, After, and Between

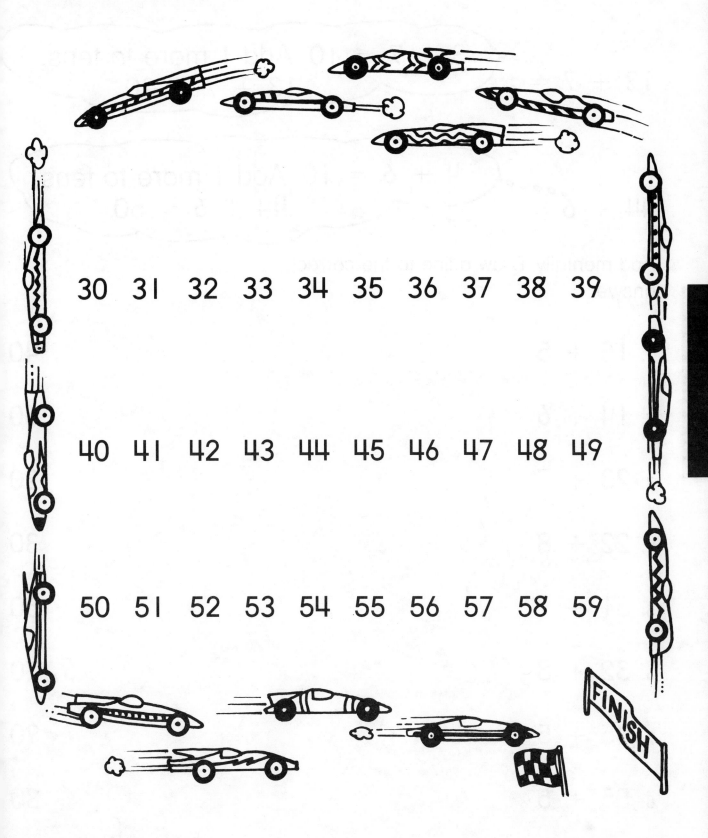

30 31 32 33 34 35 36 37 38 39

40 41 42 43 44 45 46 47 48 49

50 51 52 53 54 55 56 57 58 59

MENTAL MATH   **Complements of Multiples of 10**

$13 + 7 =$ $3 + 7 = 10$ Add 1 more to tens.
$13 + 7 = 20$

$44 + 6 =$ $4 + 6 = 10$ Add 1 more to tens.
$44 + 6 = 50$

Add mentally. Draw a line to the correct answer.

1. $15 + 5$ 40

2. $14 + 6$ 60

3. $23 + 7$ 20

4. $22 + 8$ 30

5. $51 + 9$ 50

6. $32 + 8$ 70

7. $45 + 5$ 90

8. $55 + 5$ 80

MENTAL MATH — Adding by Looking for Multiples of 10

$$8 \quad + \quad 3 \qquad\qquad 18 \quad + \quad 3$$

$$8 \quad + 2 + 1 \qquad\qquad 10 \quad + 8 \quad + 2 + 1$$
$$10 \quad + 1 = 11 \qquad\qquad 10 \quad + 10 \quad + 1$$
$$\qquad\qquad\qquad\qquad\qquad\qquad 20 \qquad\qquad + 1 = 21$$

Add mentally.

1.  2.

$$19 + 4 = \underline{\qquad} \qquad\qquad 16 + 5 = \underline{\qquad}$$

3. $55 + 6 = \underline{\qquad}$ 4. $28 + 4 = \underline{\qquad}$

5. $57 + 4 = \underline{\qquad}$ 6. $29 + 7 = \underline{\qquad}$

7. $49 + 7 = \underline{\qquad}$ 8. $38 + 3 = \underline{\qquad}$

9. $77 + 4 = \underline{\qquad}$ 10. $48 + 3 = \underline{\qquad}$

11. $55 + 8 = \underline{\qquad}$ 12. $65 + 7 = \underline{\qquad}$

13. $37 + 4 = \underline{\qquad}$ 14. $45 + 7 = \underline{\qquad}$

MENTAL MATH | Subtracting a Number from a Multiple of 10

Subtract.

1. $10 - 1 =$ _____

2. $10 - 2 =$ _____

3. $10 - 3 =$ _____

4. $10 - 4 =$ _____

5. $10 - 5 =$ _____

6. $10 - 6 =$ _____

7. $10 - 7 =$ _____

8. $10 - 8 =$ _____

9. $10 - 9 =$ _____

Subtract mentally.

10. $20 - 1 =$ _____

11. $30 - 1 =$ _____

12. $40 - 1 =$ _____

13. $30 - 5 =$ _____

14. $40 - 5 =$ _____

15. $60 - 5 =$ _____

16. $20 - 2 =$ _____

17. $70 - 2 =$ _____

18. $90 - 2 =$ _____

19. $40 - 7 =$ _____

20. $50 - 7 =$ _____

21. $80 - 7 =$ _____

22. $70 - 9 =$ _____

23. $90 - 6 =$ _____

MENTAL MATH Adding by Looking for Multiples of 10

1	2	3	4	5	6	7	8	9	10
11	12	13	14	15	16	17	18	19	20
21	22	23	24	25	26	27	28	29	30
31	32	33	34	35	36	37	38	39	40
41	42	43	44	45	46	47	48	49	50
51	52	53	54	55	56	57	58	59	60
61	62	63	64	65	66	67	68	69	70
71	72	73	74	75	76	77	78	79	80
81	82	83	84	85	86	87	88	89	90
91	92	93	94	95	96	97	98	99	100

Name _____ Date _____

Amanda has 33 toy blocks. She uses 20 of them to build a house. How many blocks does she have left?

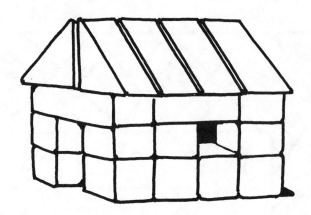

$$\begin{array}{r} 33 \\ -20 \\ \hline \end{array}$$

Amanda knows a trick for subtracting tens.

First she subtracts the tens.

$$\begin{array}{r} 3\mathbf{3} \\ -\mathbf{2}0 \\ \hline \mathbf{1} \end{array}$$

Then she brings down the ones.

$$\begin{array}{r} 3\mathbf{3} \\ -2\mathbf{0} \\ \hline 1\mathbf{3} \end{array}$$

> If you subtract 0 from a number, the difference equals that number.

Subtract mentally.

1. $\begin{array}{r} 93 \\ -40 \\ \hline \end{array}$

2. $\begin{array}{r} 53 \\ -30 \\ \hline \end{array}$

3. $\begin{array}{r} 45 \\ -40 \\ \hline \end{array}$

4. $\begin{array}{r} 87 \\ -60 \\ \hline \end{array}$

5. $\begin{array}{r} 68 \\ -30 \\ \hline \end{array}$

6. $\begin{array}{r} 75 \\ -50 \\ \hline \end{array}$

7. $\begin{array}{r} 56 \\ -10 \\ \hline \end{array}$

8. $\begin{array}{r} 83 \\ -60 \\ \hline \end{array}$

MENTAL MATH | **Adding 8 or 9 to a Number**

To add 9 to a number, add 10.
Then subtract 1.

To add 8 to a number, add 10.
Then subtract 2.

$$10 + 14 = 24$$
$$24 - 1 = 23$$

$$10 + 26 = 36$$
$$36 - 2 = 34$$

$$9 + 14 = 23$$

$$8 + 26 = 34$$

Add mentally.

1. $9 + 14 = $ _____

2. $8 + 16 = $ _____

3. $9 + 18 = $ _____

4. $8 + 19 = $ _____

5. $25 + 9 = $ _____

6. $27 + 9 = $ _____

7. $23 + 8 = $ _____

8. $26 + 9 = $ _____

9. $45 + 9 = $ _____

10. $57 + 9 = $ _____

11. $65 + 8 = $ _____

12. $83 + 9 = $ _____

13. $44 + 8 = $ _____

14. $27 + 8 = $ _____

15. $62 + 9 = $ _____

16. $17 + 9 = $ _____

17. $74 + 8 = $ _____

18. $79 + 9 = $ _____

MENTAL MATH **Recognizing Compatible Numbers**

Some pairs of numbers are easy
to add or subtract. Look for these
pairs first.

Add or subtract mentally.

1. $49 + 23 + 1 =$

$50 + 23 =$ _____

2. $83 - 29 + 29 =$

$83 - 0 =$ _____

3. $5 + 6 + 5 =$ _____

4. $9 + 9 + 1 =$ _____

5. $19 + 19 + 1 + 1 =$ _____

6. $49 + 25 - 25 =$ _____

7. $84 + 9 - 4 =$ _____

8. $28 + 28 + 2 + 2 =$ _____

9. $28 + 38 + 2 + 2 + 5 =$ _____

10. $17 + 4 + 3 + 6 =$ _____

11. $22 - 9 + 8 =$ _____

_____

MENTAL MATH ANSWER KEY

Page 1

1 more flower
4 more flowers
5 more flowers
3 more flowers
7 more flowers
2 more flowers
9 more flowers
6 more flowers

Page 2

Children will ring 14, count back 2, and write an X on 12. Children will continue to follow this procedure for each number presented and will then practice counting back 1, 2, or 3 without referring to the hundreds chart.

Page 3

Children will ring 16, count on 3, and then put an X on 19. Children will continue to follow this procedure for each number presented and will then practice counting on 1, 2, or 3 without referring to the hundreds chart.

Page 4

1. 8; 8
2. 8; 8
3. 5; 5
4. 8; 8
5. 9; 9
6. 9; 9
7. 8 8. 7 9. 2 10. 9
11. 9

Page 5

Children will respond to the clues by drawing a line through each car that did not finish the race first. Then they will ring the car (39) that won the race.

Page 6

Children will add mentally and then draw a line to each correct answer.
1. 20 2. 20 3. 30 4. 30 5. 60
6. 40 7. 50 8. 60

Page 7

1. 23 2. 21 3. 61 4. 32 5. 61
6. 36 7. 56 8. 41 9. 81
10. 51 11. 63 12. 72 13. 41
14. 52

Page 8

1. 9 2. 8 3. 7 4. 6 5. 5 6. 4
7. 3 8. 2 9. 1 10. 19 11. 29
12. 39 13. 25 14. 35 15. 55
16. 18 17. 68 18. 88 19. 33
20. 43 21. 73 22. 41 23. 51
24. 61 25. 64 26. 74 27. 84

Page 9

1. 27 2. 57 3. 77 4. 34 5. 54
6. 64 7. 45 8. 55 9. 75

Page 10

1. 53 2. 23 3. 5 4. 27 5. 38
6. 25 7. 46 8. 23

Page 11

1. 24 2. 24 3. 27 4. 27 5. 34
6. 36 7. 31 8. 35 9. 54
10. 66 11. 73 12. 92 13. 52
14. 35 15. 71 16. 26 17. 82
18. 88

Page 12

1. 73 2. 83 3. 16 4. 19 5. 40
6. 59 7. 49 8. 89 9. 60
10. 75 11. 30 12. 21

CONSUMER · Handling Money

You win 10 prize tickets at the school fair. You can trade each ticket for 1 prize. First you pick 4 finger puppets and 2 posters. Now you want to know how many more prizes you can pick.
First add. 4 + 2 = 6 prizes
Subtract. 10 − 6 = 4 prize tickets
You can pick 4 more prizes.

1. Maria wins 10 tickets at the school fair. She picks 2 balloons and 5 finger puppets. How many more prizes can Maria pick?

   _____

2. Larry wins 12 tickets at the school fair. He picks 5 balloons and 1 finger puppet. How many more prizes can Larry pick?

   _____

3. Bianca wins 11 tickets at the school fair. She picks 6 balloons and 4 finger puppets. How many more prizes can Bianca pick?

   _____

CONSUMER   Comparison Shopping

Toni buys the food with the best price. Write the cost of the food in each group from the least to the greatest. Ring each food that Toni buys.

49¢   37¢   58¢

37¢ 49¢ 58¢

1.

39¢   59¢   50¢

_____ , _____ , _____

2.

47¢   49¢   46¢

_____ , _____ , _____

3.

67¢   75¢   42¢

_____ , _____ , _____

4.

25¢   52¢   34¢

_____ , _____ , _____

5.

89¢   78¢   83¢

_____ , _____ , _____

6.

98¢   61¢   89¢

_____ , _____ , _____

CONSUMER **Keeping Records**

Keep track of how much you spend in a week.
Write down the cost of each thing. Then add to find the total.

1. You buy a pencil that costs
   9¢. You buy an eraser that
   costs 3¢. You buy a ruler that
   costs 5¢.

WEEK 1	
Pencil	9¢
Eraser	¢
Ruler	¢
Total	¢

2. You buy a pen that costs 6¢.
   You buy a crayon that costs
   5¢. You buy a pad that costs
   7¢.

WEEK 2	
Pen	¢
Crayon	¢
Pad	¢
Total	¢

3. You buy a book that costs 8¢.
   You buy a ribbon that costs
   4¢. You buy a sticker that
   costs 4¢.

WEEK 3	
Book	¢
Ribbon	¢
Sticker	¢
Total	¢

4. You buy some paint that costs
   5¢. You buy tape that costs
   7¢. You buy a magnet that
   costs 4¢.

WEEK 4	
Paint	¢
Tape	¢
Magnet	¢
Total	¢

5. In which week did you spend the most money?
   Week _____

CONSUMER   The Better Buy

Which store has the better price? Subtract to find how much you save. Ring the store with the better price.

$$\underline{10¢} - \underline{6¢} = \underline{4¢}$$

1.

___¢ − ___¢ = ___¢

2.

___¢ − ___¢ = ___¢

3.

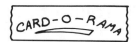

___¢ − ___¢ = ___¢

4.

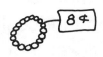

___¢ − ___¢ = ___¢

5.

___¢ − ___¢ = ___¢

6.

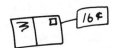

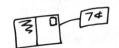

___¢ − ___¢ = ___¢

CONSUMER — Time and Money

Sometimes you can rent things by the hour. Write the number of hours you rent for. Then add the coins to find how much it costs to rent each thing.

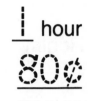

$\underline{1}$ hour

$80¢$

1.

_____ hours

_____ ¢

2.

_____ hours

_____ ¢

3.

_____ hours

_____ ¢

4.

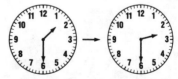

_____ hour

_____ ¢

CONSUMER   Saving Money

Children often save their money in banks.
Look at the table. Add the money to see how
much each child saves. Write the amount.

$$\begin{array}{r} 43¢ \\ 12¢ \\ + 15¢ \\ \hline 70¢ \end{array}$$

Rahim				
Fatima	61¢	26¢	12¢	_____
Ken	48¢	37¢	11¢	_____
Junior	29¢	51¢	14¢	_____
Hiromi	52¢	19¢	14¢	_____

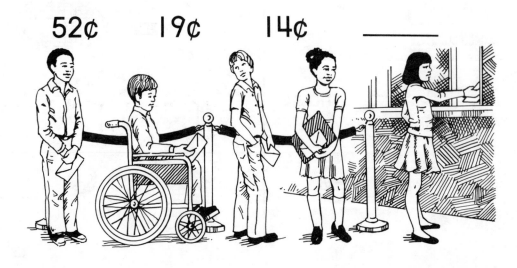

Use after pages 161–162.

CONSUMER Saving Money

Coupons can help you save money. You might want to buy a toothbrush that costs 95¢. You have a toothbrush coupon for 10¢. You can buy the toothbrush for 85¢. Subtract to find the price you pay for each item.

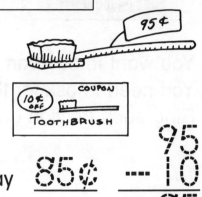

You pay 85¢

$$\begin{array}{r} 95 \\ -10 \\ \hline 85 \end{array}$$

1.
55¢

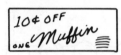
10¢ OFF
ONE Muffin

You pay ___.

2.
91¢

23¢ OFF
PAINT BOX
STORE COUPON

You pay ___.

3.
75¢

ORANGE JUICE
16¢ OFF
1 CARTON
ORANGE JUICE

You pay ___.

4.
68¢

37¢ OFF LIGHT BULB
STORE COUPON *

You pay ___.

5.
84¢

CEREAL
12¢ OFF
ONE BOX
CEREAL

You pay ___.

6.
90¢

STRAW
HAT
41¢ OFF

You pay ___.

Name _____ Date _____

You want to buy part of something.
You need to ask for the fraction you want.
Ring each fraction of food.

You want to buy $\frac{1}{4}$ of the squash.

1. You want to buy $\frac{5}{10}$ of the apples.

2. You want to buy $\frac{1}{4}$ of the eggs.

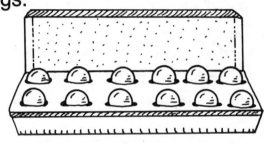

3. You want to buy $\frac{4}{6}$ of the cheese.

4. You want to buy $\frac{3}{4}$ of the butter.

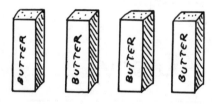

5. You want to buy $\frac{1}{4}$ of the watermelon.

6. You want to buy $\frac{7}{8}$ of the carrots.

Name _____ Date _____

Sandra is drawing a picture. She wants to put yarn around each shape. Use your ruler to find the perimeter of each shape. How many inches of yarn does Sandra need to buy for each shape?

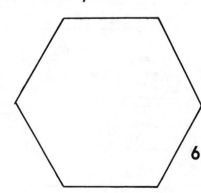

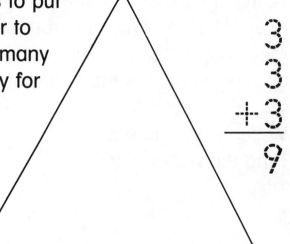

$$\begin{array}{r} 3 \\ 3 \\ +3 \\ \hline 9 \end{array}$$

1. Sandra needs to buy ____ inches of yarn.

2. Sandra needs to buy ____ inches of yarn.

3. Sandra needs to buy ____ inches of yarn.

4. Sandra needs to buy ____ inches of yarn.

5. Sandra needs to buy ____ inches of yarn.

6. Sandra needs to buy ____ inches of yarn.

CONSUMER Unit Shopping

Sometimes two packages of the same product
have different amounts. Yet, the packages
may cost the same. The package with the
greater amount is the better buy.

Write > or < in each ◯.
Ring the better buy.

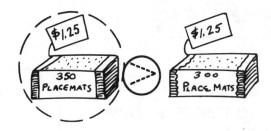

1.

2.

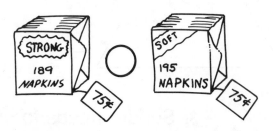

3.

4.

5.

6.

CONSUMER **Unit Shopping**

Many things are sold in large packages. Sometimes you have to buy more than you need. Subtract to find how many extras you have.

You buy

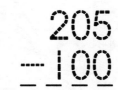

You need
100

$$\begin{array}{r} 205 \\ -100 \\ \hline \end{array}$$

How many extras? $\underline{105}$

---

1. You buy

You need
430

How many extras? _____

2. You buy

You need
447

How many extras? _____

---

3. You buy

You need
111

How many extras? _____

4. You buy

You need
100

How many extras? _____

---

5. You buy

You need
201

How many extras? _____

6. You buy

You need
136

How many extras? _____

CONSUMER **Shopping**

Each vegetable or fruit has a price. You want to
buy more than one of each. Fill in each price.
Find how much money you need.

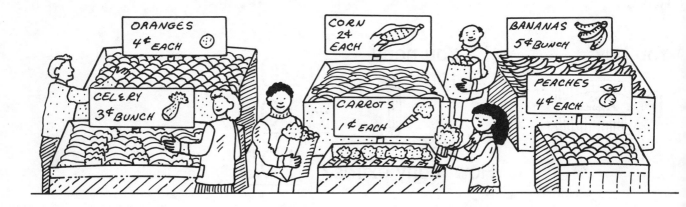

1. 2 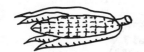 × <u>2¢</u> each = <u>4¢</u>

2. 5  × _____ each = _____

3. 3   × _____ each bunch = _____

4. 4 ⬭ × _____ each = _____

5. 2  × _____ each = _____

6. 3 ◯ × _____ each = _____

CONSUMER ANSWER KEY

Page 1

1. 3 prizes
2. 6 prizes
3. 1 prize

Page 2

1. 39¢, 50¢, 59¢; 39¢
2. 46¢, 47¢, 49¢; 46¢
3. 42¢; 67¢, 75¢; 42¢
4. 25¢, 34¢, 52¢; 25¢
5. 78¢, 83¢, 89¢; 78¢
6. 61¢, 89¢, 98¢; 61¢

Page 3

1. 9¢ + 3¢ + 5¢ = 17¢
2. 6¢ + 5¢ + 7¢ = 18¢
3. 8¢ + 4¢ + 4¢ = 16¢
4. 5¢ + 7¢ + 4¢ = 16¢

Page 4

1. Disco Disk; 6¢
2. The Gift Shop; 2¢
3. The Paper Shop; 8¢
4. Sabrina's; 8¢
5. Food World; 9¢
6. Hilltown Supply; 9¢

Page 5

1. 2 hours; 92¢
2. 2 hours; 50¢
3. 3 hours; 58¢
4. 1 hour; 94¢

Page 6

1. 99¢ 2. 96¢ 3. 94¢ 4. 85¢

Page 7

1. 45¢ 2. 68¢ 3. 59¢ 4. 31¢
5. 72¢ 6. 49¢

Page 8

1. $\frac{5}{10}$

2. $\frac{1}{4}$

3. $\frac{4}{6}$

4. $\frac{3}{4}$

5. $\frac{1}{4}$

6. $\frac{7}{8}$

Page 9

1. 6 inches
2. 4 inches
3. 3 inches
4. 8 inches
5. 8 inches
6. 6 inches

Page 10

1. >; 450 super paper plates
2. <; 195 soft napkins
3. >; 131 bowls
4. <; 502 cups
5. <; 250 spoons
6. >; 316 forks

Page 11

1. 110
2. 212
3. 414
4. 200
5. 201
6. 136

Page 12

2. 1¢; 5¢
3. 5¢; 15¢
4. 4¢; 16¢
5. 3¢; 6¢
6. 4¢; 12¢

Name _____ Date _____

Always turn a calculator on
before using it.   Press:

The calculator should show   **0.**

How many digits can appear on
the calculator?

Press:

_____

Clear the calculator.   Press:

The calculator should show   **0.**

Now press:

Turn the calculator display upside down. What
do the numbers say? Write the word.

_____

Clear the calculator. Turn it off.

CALCULATOR — Adding and Subtracting

Here is how to add with a calculator.

Turn the calculator on.   Add 31 + 28.

Press:

The calculator should show 59.

Clear the calculator.

Subtract with a calculator.   Subtract 46 − 25.

Press:

The calculator should show 21.

Use a calculator to solve.

1. $13 + 35 = $ ___   2. $67 - 29 = $ ___

3. $19 - 7 = $ ___   4. $7 + 96 = $ ___

5. $34 - 17 = $ ___   6. $22 + 58 = $ ___

CALCULATOR   The Calculator Speaks

You can show words on a calculator.

Press:

Now turn the calculator display upside down.
Read what you see. It looks like the word
SELL.

Press the numbers. Turn the calculator upside
down and write the word you see.

1.

2.

_____

_____

3.

4.

_____

_____

5.

6.

_____

_____

CALCULATOR — Skip-Counting

Use a calculator to skip-count by 5's.
Press:

Try this shortcut on your calculator.
Press:

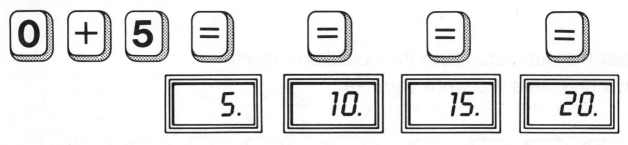

Use a calculator to skip-count across the stars
by 7. Start at 0. Count the stars. Write the
number that the calculator shows in the
correct star.

CALCULATOR — Order in the Court!

Is 6 + 4 the same as 4 + 6?
Use a calculator to find out.

Press:  10.

Press: 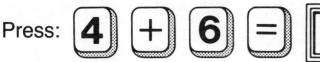 10.

1. Are the answers the same? _____

Use a calculator to find if 6 − 4
is the same as 4 − 6.

2. Are the answers the same? _____

In addition, the order of the
numbers doesn't matter.

In subtraction, the order of the
numbers cannot be changed
without changing the answers.

Use a calculator to solve. Fill in the circles
next to the problems where the order can be
changed for the same answer.

3. ◯ 5 + 6 = ____

4. ◯ 89 − 5 = ____

5. ◯ 56 − 42 = ____

6. ◯ 14 + 23 = ____

Name _____ Date _____

Use a calculator to solve. Write the answer in front of the picture.

1. Phillip had 26 . Then 14 rolled away. How many are left?

_____ 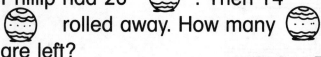 are left.

2. Caryl picked 62 .
Sammy picked 19 .
How many did they pick in all?

They picked _____ in all.

3. DeeDee had 19 . Then 11 blew away. How many are left?

_____ are left.

Name _____ Date _____

CALCULATOR   **Down the Line**

Use a calculator to complete the problem. Follow
the directions on the left side of the box.

START	14		
Add	3	=	17
Subtract	11	=	6
Add	24	=	
Subtract	10	=	
Subtract	14	=	

START	35		
Subtract	4	=	
Subtract	12	=	
Add	16	=	
Add	26	=	
Subtract	34	=	

START	25		
Add	25	=	
Add	16	=	
Subtract	28	=	
Subtract	17	=	

START	42		
Add	14	=	
Subtract	19	=	
Subtract	14	=	
Add	37	=	

CALCULATOR   Rockin' Robin

Add or subtract with a calculator. Then look at
the chart. See what color goes with each
answer. Follow the chart and color in the
picture.

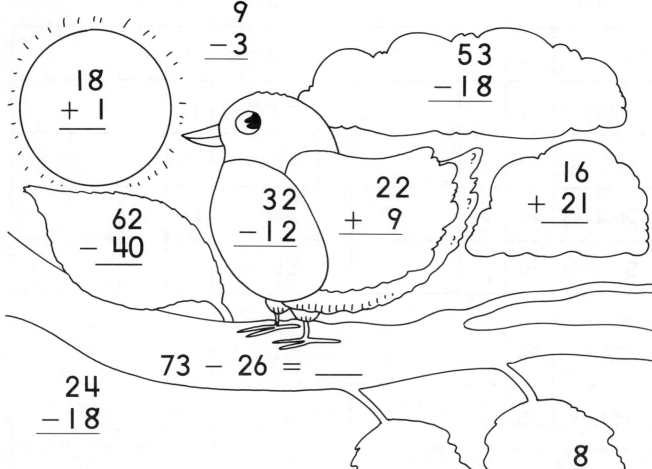

$$\begin{array}{r} 9 \\ -3 \\ \hline \end{array}$$

$$\begin{array}{r} 18 \\ +\ 1 \\ \hline \end{array}$$

$$\begin{array}{r} 53 \\ -18 \\ \hline \end{array}$$

$$\begin{array}{r} 62 \\ -40 \\ \hline \end{array}$$

$$\begin{array}{r} 32 \\ -12 \\ \hline \end{array}$$

$$\begin{array}{r} 22 \\ +\ 9 \\ \hline \end{array}$$

$$\begin{array}{r} 16 \\ +21 \\ \hline \end{array}$$

$$73 - 26 = \underline{\qquad}$$

$$\begin{array}{r} 24 \\ -18 \\ \hline \end{array}$$

$$\begin{array}{r} 47 \\ -18 \\ \hline \end{array}$$

$$\begin{array}{r} 8 \\ +15 \\ \hline \end{array}$$

Blue 1 to 10	Red 11 to 20
Green 21 to 30	Gray 31 to 40
Brown 41 to 50	

CALCULATOR   **Distance in a Duchy**

Use a calculator to add the kilometers.

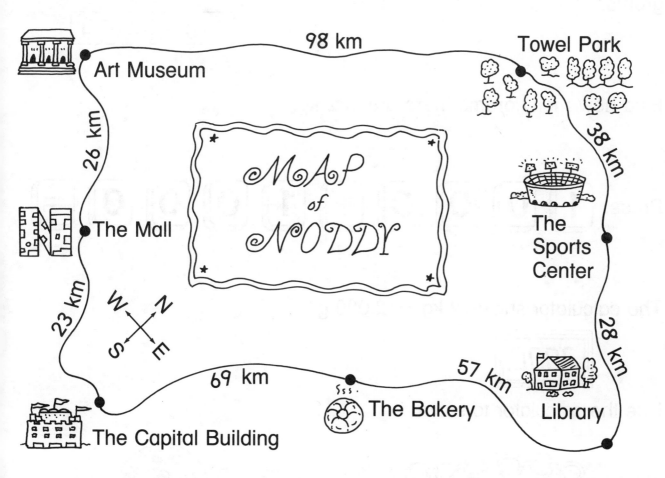

1. How many kilometers is it from the Art Museum to Towel Park to the Sports Center?

_____

2. How many kilometers is it from the Bakery to the Library to the Sports Center?

_____

3. How many kilometers is it from the Capitol Building to the Mall to the Art Museum?

_____

4. How many kilometers is it from Towel Park to the Art Museum to the Mall?

_____

CALCULATOR   **Weight Change**

Use a calculator to change from kilograms to grams.

| 1 kg = 1,000 g |

Find how many grams there are in 2 kg.

Press:

The calculator shows 2 kg = 2,000 g

Use the calculator to solve

1.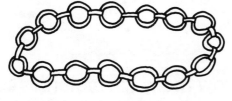

3 kg = _____g

2.

4 kg = _____g

3.

5 kg = _____g

4.

6 kg = _____g

CALCULATOR **Grand Prix Total**

Use a calculator to add or subtract the two car
numbers. Write the answer on the car in front
of the two cars. Keep going until you find the
number of the lead car.

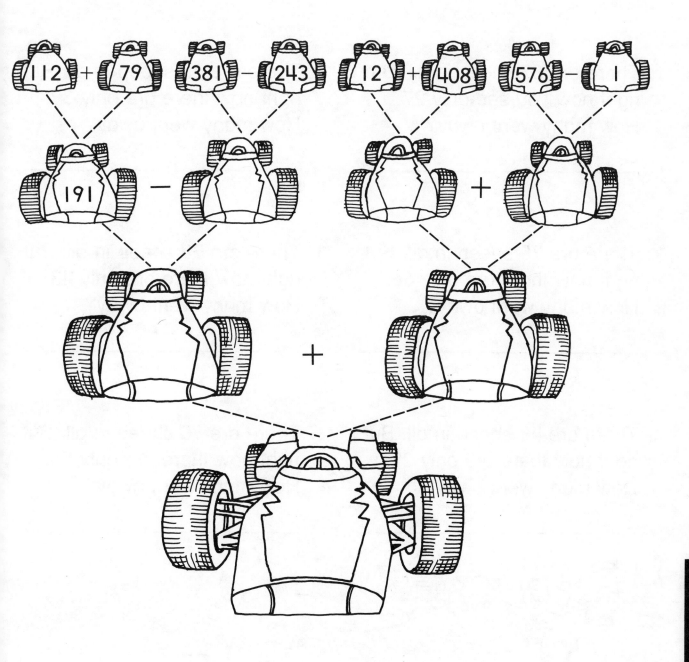

CALCULATOR   Counting Sheep

Pretend it is your job to count sheep.
Sometimes groups of sheep wander into the
woods. Subtract with a calculator to find how
many sheep leave.

1. There are 87 sheep in all. But
right now you see only 27.
How many went away?

   _____

2. There are 65 sheep in all. But
right now there are only 39.
How many went away?

   _____

3. There are 75 sheep in all. But
right now there are only 66.
How many went away?

   _____

4. There are 78 sheep in all. But
right now there are only 43.
How many went away?

   _____

5. There are 48 sheep in all. But
right now there are only 29.
How many went away?

   _____

6. There are 95 sheep in all. But
right now there are only 56.
How many went away?

   _____

CALCULATOR   Into the Lion's Den

Help the lion cub find its way home. Use a
calculator to add and subtract. The path
follows the answer 666.

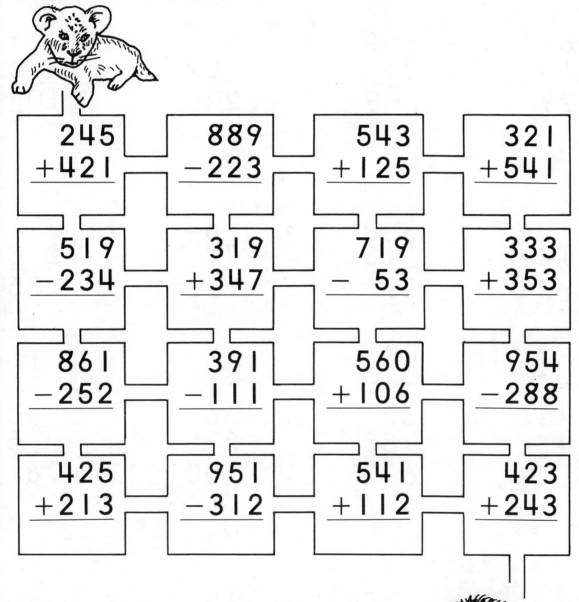

245 +421	889 −223	543 +125	321 +541
519 −234	319 +347	719 − 53	333 +353
861 −252	391 −111	560 +106	954 −288
425 +213	951 −312	541 +112	423 +243

CALCULATOR   **Whizz Quizz**

Use a calculator to find the missing numbers.

1.
```
   36 9
 +4 1 0
  7 79
```

2.
```
   6 _8
 +21 _
  _49
```

3.
```
   6 _4
 - _52
   24 _
```

4.
```
   _ 11
 - 8 _1
   10
```

5.
```
   81 _
 + _14
   9 _3
```

6.
```
   3 _0
 - _18
   20 _
```

7.
```
   _64
 +71 _
   9 _3
```

8.
```
   87 _
 -2 _8
   _06
```

9.
```
   _40
 +64 _
   8 _0
```

10.
```
   82 _
 - _55
   6 _2
```

11.
```
   56 _
 -2 _5
   _00
```

12.
```
   _50
 - _5
   76 _
```

13.
```
   29 _
 + _09
   9 _3
```

14.
```
   _35
 -64 _
   1 _0
```

15.
```
   12 _
 + _68
   4 _7
```

16.
```
   _85
 +2 _5
   97
```

CALCULATOR   There Are Many

Use a calculator to solve. Write the answer in front of the picture.

1. Alexis has 945 🐚 .
   She puts 296 🐚 away.
   How many 🐚 are left?   There are _____ 🐚 left.

2. There are 354 🪙 in a bag,
   110 🪙 in a box, and 462
   coins in a drawer. How many
   coins are there in all?   There are _____ 🪙 in all.

3. Jim has 980 🌰 .
   He uses 265 🌰 .
   How many 🌰 are left?   _____ 🌰 are left.

CALCULATOR   **Fraction Action**

To show a fraction on a calculator, you must use a decimal. When you write a decimal, be sure to use a decimal point (.).

$$\frac{1}{10} = 0.1 \qquad\qquad \frac{2}{10} = 0.2$$

Write a decimal to show the missing part of the turkey pot pie.

1.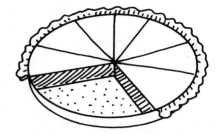

_____

2.

_____

3.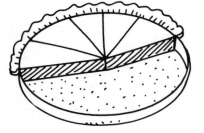

_____

4.

_____

CALCULATOR   Money, Money, Money

To show money on a calculator,
use the decimal point

Show: $18.03

See: | 0. |

Press:

Write: $1.80

Write the numbers on the calculator keys to
show the amount of money.

1. **$20.09**

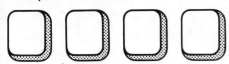

2. **$2.80**

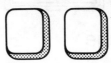

3. **$2.09**

☐☐☐☐

4. **$29.00**

☐☐

Write the numbers as dollars and cents.

5. | 65. | _____

6. | 3.82 | _____

7. | 6.5 | _____

8. | 382. | _____

9. | .65 | _____

10. | 38.2 | _____

CALCULATOR   Making Change

Use a calculator to find how much change you get when you buy something. Use the decimal point [·] to show money on a calculator.

A baseball costs $3.89. If you pay for the ball with a $5 bill, how much change do you get back?

Subtract $5.00 − $3.89.

Press: [5] [−] [3] [·] [8] [9] [=]

The calculator shows | 1.11 |

You get $1.11 in change.

Use a calculator to solve.

	Pay	Cost	Change		Pay	Cost	Change
1.	$8.50 − $8.03 = _____			2.	$10.00 − $7.26 = _____		
3.	$5.00 − $0.50 = _____			4.	$15.25 − $15.07 = _____		
5.	$20.00 − $1.72 = _____			6.	$50.00 − $33.33 = _____		

CALCULATOR Read and Press

Write the addition problem. Use a calculator to
add the numbers.

Twenty-one, forty-three, two
Press:

1. Six hundred, two hundred
twelve, five

___ + ___ + ___ = [ ]

2. Four hundred eleven, one
hundred four, ninety-four

___ + ___ + ___ = [ ]

3. Seven hundred seven, eighty-
seven, seventy-eight

___ + ___ + ___ = [ ]

4. Three hundred forty-four, six,
twenty-five

___ + ___ + ___ = [ ]

5. Five hundred fifty, sixty-five,
two hundred five

___ + ___ + ___ = [ ]

6. Thirty-nine, eleven, six
hundred ninety-two

___ + ___ + ___ = [ ]

7. Three hundred one, ten, nine

___ + ___ + ___ = [ ]

CALCULATOR   The Land of Scrubbscrubb!

People from Scrubbscrubb measure in rungs.
Use a calculator to find each distance in the
Land of Scrubbscrubb.

1. The Ancient Wall is 75 rungs
   long. The perimeter of Old
   Scrubb Castle is 29 rungs less
   than the wall. How many
   rungs is the perimeter of the
   castle?

   _____

2. The River Skratch is 24 rungs
   longer than the Ancient Wall.
   The River Skratch is
   rungs long.   _____

3. The perimeter of the James R.
   Spackle Lake is 45 rungs
   longer than the Ancient Wall.
   How many rungs is the
   perimeter of the lake?   _____

CALCULATOR   **More Fraction Action**

To show a fraction on a calculator, you must use a decimal. Change a fraction to a decimal by dividing the top part of the fraction by the bottom part.

 is a division sign.

$$\frac{1}{2} = 1 \div 2 \qquad\qquad \frac{3}{8} = 3 \div 8$$

Press:    Press:

The calculator shows $\boxed{0.5}$ The calculator shows $\boxed{0.375}$

$$\frac{1}{2} = 0.5 \qquad\qquad \frac{3}{8} = 0.375$$

Use a calculator to change the fraction to a decimal.

1. $\dfrac{1}{2} =$ _____   2. $\dfrac{1}{8} =$ _____

3. $\dfrac{7}{10} =$ _____   4. $\dfrac{3}{4} =$ _____

5. $\dfrac{5}{8} =$ _____   6. $\dfrac{3}{6} =$ _____

CALCULATOR   Subtracting Prices

Use a calculator to find the difference between
the costs of the plants.

1. A palm plant costs 59¢. A fern
costs 47¢. How much more
does the palm plant cost?

_____

2. A marigold plant costs 75¢. A
lily costs 69¢. How much
more does the marigold plant
cost?

_____

3. A geranium costs 46¢. A
peony costs 38¢. How much
more does the geranium cost?

_____

4. A cactus costs 58¢. A
Venus's-flytrap costs 39¢.
How much more does the
cactus cost?

_____

5. A spider plant costs 87¢. A
jade plant costs 78¢. How
much more does the spider
plant cost?

_____

6. A tulip costs 74¢. A crocus
costs 66¢. How much more
does a tulip cost?

_____

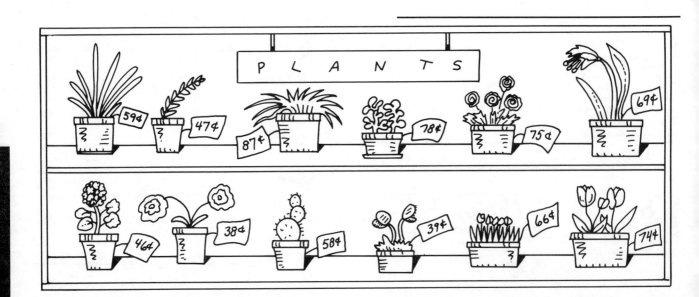

CALCULATOR   Addition as Multiplication

Add 5 four times: 5 + 5 + 5 + 5

Press:

10.	15.	20.

Adding 5 four times is the same as multiplying 5 by 4.

$$5 + 5 + 5 + 5 = 5 \times 4 = 20$$

Use a calculator to add. Then write the problem as a multiplication sentence.

1. 7 + 7 + 7 + 7 + 7 + 7 + 7 = _____

2. 15 + 15 + 15 + 15 + 15 + 15 = _____

3. 38 + 38 + 38 + 38 + 38 + 38 + 38 + 38 =

   _____

4. 56 + 56 + 56 + 56 = _____

5. 109 + 109 + 109 + 109 + 109 = _____

CALCULATOR **Multiplying and Dividing**

Here is how to multiply with a calculator.

Multiply 12 × 3 = _____.

Press:

The calculator shows | **36.** |

Here is how to divide with a calculator.

Divide 3)$\overline{72}$.

Press:

The calculator shows | **24.** |

Use a calculator to solve.

1. 25 × 31 = ___

2. 12 × 18 = ___

3. 43 × 5 = ___

4. 4)$\overline{88}$

5. 9)$\overline{288}$

6. 7)$\overline{161}$

7. 19 × 47 = ___

8. 72 × 9 = ___

9. 50 × 7 = ___

CALCULATOR ANSWER KEY

Page 1

Answers will vary, but most calculators display eight.
H1

Page 2

1. 48
2. 38
3. 12
4. 103
5. 17
6. 80

Page 3

1. SOIL
2. HILL
3. LOOSE
4. LEGS
5. BIG
6. BOIL

Page 4

14; 21; 28; 35

Page 5

1. yes 2. no 3. 11 4. 84
5. 14 6. 37

Page 6

1. 12 2. 81 3. 8

Page 7

30; 20; 6
31; 19; 35; 61; 27
50; 66; 38; 21
56; 37; 23; 60

Page 8

6; 6; 20; 35
31; 37; 19
17; 22; 29; 23
47

Page 9

1. 136 km
2. 85 km
3. 48 km
4. 124 km

Page 10

1. 3,000 g
2. 4,000 g
3. 5,000 g
4. 6,000 g

Page 11

191; 138; 420; 575
53; 995
1,048

Page 12

1. 60 2. 26 3. 9 4. 35 5. 19
6. 39

Page 13

666; 666; 666; 666; 666; 666;
666; 666
668; 862; 285; 686; 609; 280; 638
639; 671; 653

Page 14

1. 7 2. 8 3. 2 4. 0 5. 3 6. 2
7. 8 8. 6 9. 8 10. 7 11. 3
12. 5 13. 0 14. 9 15. 9 16. 0

Page 15

1. 649 2. 926 3. 715

Page 16

1. 0.3 2. 0.4 3. 0.5 4. 0.6

Page 17

1. 20.09 2. 2.8 3. 2.09 4. 29
5. $65.00 6. $3.82 7. $6.50
8. $382.00 9. $0.65 10. $38.20

Page 18

1. $0.47 2. $2.74 3. $4.41
4. $0.18 5. 18.28 6. 16.67

Page 19

1. $600 + 212 + 5 = 817$
2. $411 + 104 + 94 = 609$
3. $707 + 87 + 78 = 872$
4. $344 + 6 + 25 = 375$
5. $550 + 65 + 205 = 820$
6. $39 + 11 + 692 = 742$
7. $301 + 10 + 9 = 320$

Page 20

1. 46 2. 99 3. 120

Page 21

1. 0.5 2. 0.125 3. 0.7 4. 0.75
5. 0.625 6. 0.5

Page 22

1. 12¢ 2. 6¢ 3. 8¢ 4. 19¢
5. 9¢ 6. 8¢

Page 23

1. $49; 7 \times 7 = 49$
2. $90; 15 \times 6 = 90$
3. $304; 38 \times 8 = 304$
4. $124; 4 \times 56 = 124$
5. $545; 109 \times 5 = 545$

Page 24

1. 775 2. 216 3. 215 4. 22
5. 32 6. 23 7. 893 8. 648
9. 350

COMPUTER **The Keyboard**

Your teacher will show you how to turn on the computer. The flashing box on the screen is the **cursor.** It tells you that the computer is waiting for you to type.

Find the letters of your name. Type them. Find the **RETURN** key. Press it. The computer will beep and print something on the screen. Don't worry about it.

The ″ is on the same key as a number. Find it. Find the **SHIFT** key. Hold down the SHIFT key while you press the ″ key 5 times. Press the RETURN key 12 times. Watch the lines move up the screen.

1. Is the RETURN key on the left side or the right side of the keyboard?

_____

2. What is the computer waiting for when the flashing box is on the screen?

_____

3. What is the flashing box called?

_____

4. Which number is on the same key as the ″ symbol?

_____

COMPUTER   BASIC #1

The computer does what you tell it to do. The computer understands only when you use a language called BASIC.

Type this.
    PRINT "HELLO"

Press the RETURN key. You will see this.
    HELLO

Good work! You just wrote a BASIC statement.

When you use the PRINT statement with " ", the computer prints what is between " and ".

Type each BASIC command, and press RETURN. Write what the computer prints.

I. PRINT "ABCDEFG" _____   2. PRINT "12345" _____

3. PRINT "RED SHOES" _____   4. PRINT "2 DOGS" _____

5. PRINT "FAT PENS" _____   6. PRINT "2 FOR 1" _____

COMPUTER   BASIC #2

Find the + key on the computer keyboard.
Type this and then press the RETURN key.
    PRINT "4 + 4"

1. What does the computer print? _____
It typed what was between the " ". Type this
and then press RETURN.
    PRINT 4 + 4

The computer does the math and prints 8.

When you use the PRINT statement with
numbers and signs but no " ", the
computer will do the math for you.

Read each PRINT statement. Write what you
think the computer will print for each
command.

2. PRINT 6 − 2 _____   **3.** PRINT "5 + 4" _____

4. PRINT "1234" _____   **5.** PRINT 3 + 6 _____

COMPUTER BASIC #3

A **PROGRAM** is a set of computer commands.
When you run a PROGRAM, all the
commands are done, one right after the other.

To begin, type **NEW** to clear the computer's
memory. Press RETURN. Now type this, and
press RETURN after each line.
    10 PRINT "HERE IS MY"
    20 PRINT "FIRST PROGRAM"

Next type **LIST** and then press RETURN. The
program will show on the screen. If you made
any mistakes, you can correct them now.

Type RUN and then press RETURN. Write
what you see.

_____

_____

1. What do you type to clear the
   computer's memory?

2. What do you type to see the
   program in memory?

_____ _____

COMPUTER BASIC #4

You can use PRINT commands to tell the computer to show different things on the screen.

Type NEW and then press RETURN to clear the computer's memory. Next type this, and press RETURN after each line.

    10 PRINT 1 + 1
    20 PRINT 6 − 1

Type RUN and then press RETURN. You will see this.

    2
    5

When you do not use " " in the PRINT command, the computer will perform the operation you type.

1. Clear the computer's memory. Type this program.

    10 PRINT 3 + 2
    20 PRINT 5 − 1

  Run the program. Write what you see.

2. Clear the memory again. Type this program.

    10 PRINT 8 − 6
    20 PRINT 10 − 4

  Run the program. Write what you see.

_____

_____

COMPUTER BASIC #5

Type NEW and then press RETURN. This clears the computer's memory. Now type this.

10 PRINT "3 + 3 = "
20 PRINT 3 + 3

Type RUN and press RETURN. You will see this.

3 + 3 =
6

The program has two PRINT statements. The first one has " ". The second one does not.

Look at this program. Do not type it.

10 PRINT 6 − 5
20 PRINT 1 + 1
30 PRINT 7 − 4
40 PRINT "GO"

If you ran this program, what would you see?

_____

_____

_____

_____

Now try the program to test your answer.

COMPUTER   BASIC #6

Type NEW and then press RETURN to clear the computer's memory. Type this program. Press RETURN at the end of each line.

    10 PRINT "MY DOG HAS"
    20 PRINT "SPOTS"

Each line of the program begins with a **line number.** The computer does the commands in the order of the line numbers.

RUN the program. Type RUN and then press RETURN. Write what is typed on the screen.

_____

_____

LIST the program. Type LIST and then press RETURN. Write what you see on the screen.

_____

_____

You can add a line to the program between lines 10 and 20. You can use any number between 10 and 20. Let's use 15. Type this and then press RETURN.

    15 PRINT "BIG"

LIST your program again. This time you will see this.

    10 PRINT "MY DOG HAS"
    15 PRINT "BIG"
    20 PRINT "SPOTS"

RUN the program. What is typed on the screen?

_____

_____

_____

COMPUTER   BASIC #7

How do you clear the computer's memory?

Type _____ Press _____

Clear the computer's memory. Type this program. Press RETURN at the end of each line.

    20 PRINT "OF YOUR"
    10 PRINT "TAKE CARE"
    30 PRINT "HAIR"

How do you RUN the program?

Type _____ Press _____

RUN the program. Write what is printed on the screen.

_____

_____

_____

How do you LIST the program?

Type _____ Press _____

LIST the program.

How do you make the computer print this on the screen?

    TAKE CARE
    OF YOUR
    LOVELY
    HAIR

Type _____

Press _____

Type this and then press RETURN. LIST your program again. RUN the program. Write what you see on the screen.

_____

_____

_____

_____

    Use after pages 221–222.

COMPUTER   **Logo #1**

Write the commands that tell the turtle to go
forward 30 steps and to turn right 90.

_____

_____

Try the commands on a
computer. Put them into the
computer four times. What shape
does the turtle draw? Draw it in
the box.

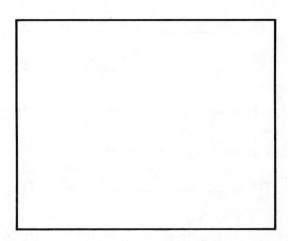

Type these commands on a
computer. What shape does the
turtle draw? Draw it in the box.

FD 50
RT 45
FD 30
RT 45
FD 30
RT 45
FD 30
RT 45
FD 50

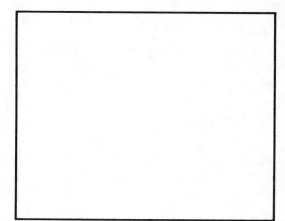

COMPUTER   Logo #2

These are the commands to draw the picture.

FD 30	FD 30	FD 30	FD 30	FD 30
FD 30	FD 30	FD 30	LT 45	LT 45
RT 90	RT 90	RT 90	RT 45	RT 45

The commands are out of order. Write them in the correct order.

a. _____   b. _____   c. _____

d. _____   e. _____   f. _____

g. _____   h. _____   i. _____

j. _____   k. _____   l. _____

m. _____   n. _____   o. _____

Now try the commands, as you ordered them, on a computer. They should draw the picture shown on this page. If they do not, fix them.

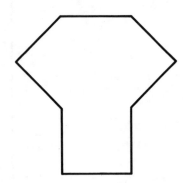

COMPUTER   Logo #3

Write the commands to draw the picture. Use
FD, BK, RT, and LT. The turtle always turns
45. The turtle steps are marked on the picture.

Write the commands on the lines.

a. _____   b. _____   c. _____   d. _____
e. _____   f. _____   g. _____   h. _____
i. _____   j. _____   k. _____   l. _____
m. _____   n. _____   o. _____   p. _____
q. _____   r. _____   s. _____   t. _____
u. _____

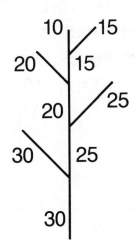

COMPUTER   Logo #4

Write the commands to draw the picture. Use
REPEAT to write the commands on one line.
The turtle always moves 40 steps. It always
turns 40 degrees.

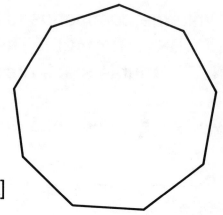

REPEAT _____ [_____]

Try the commands on a computer. They
should draw the same picture. If they do not,
fix them.

What happens if you REPEAT a REPEAT
command? Try it. Write a command to
REPEAT the commands that you just wrote. It
should REPEAT them twice, and turn 180
degrees between them.

REPEAT _____

Type the commands on a computer. What
shape does the turtle draw? Draw it in the
box.

COMPUTER ANSWER KEY

Page 1

1. the right side
2. for you to type
3. the cursor
4. 2; IBM—the ´ symbol

Page 2

1. ABCDEFG
2. RED SHOES
3. FAT PENS
4. 12345
5. 2 DOGS
6. 2 FOR 1

Page 3

1. 4 + 4
2. 4
3. 5 + 4
4. 1234
5. 9

Page 4

HERE IS MY
FIRST PROGRAM
1. NEW
2. LIST

Page 5

1. 5, 4
2. 2, 6

Page 6

1
2
3
GO

Page 7

MY DOG HAS SPOTS
10 PRINT "MY DOG HAS"
20 PRINT "SPOTS"
MY DOG HAS
BIG
SPOTS

Page 8

NEW RETURN
RUN RETURN
TAKE CARE
OF YOUR
HAIR
LIST RETURN
25 PRINT "LOVELY"
RETURN
TAKE CARE
OF YOUR
LOVELY
HAIR

Page 9

FD 30
RT 90
Check children's art.

Page 10

a. FD 30 **b.** LT 45 **c.** FD 30
d. RT 90 **e.** FD 30 **f.** RT 45
g. FD 30 **h.** RT 45 **i.** FD 30
j. RT 90 **k.** FD 30 **l.** FT 45
m. FD 30 **n.** RT 90 **o.** FD 30
Check children's art.

Page 11

a. FD 30 **b.** LT 45 **c.** FD 30
d. BK 30 **e.** RT 45 **f.** FD 25
g. RT 45 **h.** FD 25 **i.** BK 25
j. LT 45 **k.** FD 20 **l.** LT 45
m. FD 20 **n.** BK 20 **o.** RT 45
p. FD 15 **q.** RT 45 **r.** FD 15
s. BK 15 **t.** LT 45 **u.** FD 10
Answers may vary.
Chart: 10, 15, 15, 20, 20,
25, 25, 30, 30

Page 12

9 [FD 40 RT 10]
Check children's art.
2 [REPEAT 9 [FD 40 RT 40]
RT 180]
Check children's art.

CHAPTERS 1–6   Speed Drill
Use after each textbook chapter.   No student page.
*These drills can be used with the first six chapters to improve
students' listening skills. Tell students that you will read each
problem two times. They will write the answer to the problem on a
separate sheet of paper.*

CHAPTER 1
1. 3 plus 6 minus 5 _____
2. 8 minus 6 plus 6 _____
3. 11 minus 7 plus 3 _____
4. 2 plus 3 plus 4 _____
5. 4 plus 5 minus 3 plus 6 _____
6. 3 minus 2 plus 2 minus 1 plus 4 _____

CHAPTER 2
1. One more than 21 _____
2. One more than 53 _____
3. One less than 63 _____
4. The number between 86 and 88 _____
5. The number between 29 and 31 _____

CHAPTER 3
1. 9 plus 7 _____
2. 5 plus 1 plus 3 _____
3. 2 plus 6 plus 6 _____
4. 8 plus 7 plus 1 _____
5. 5 minus 4 plus 8 plus 5 plus 1 _____

CHAPTER 4
1. 15 minus 8 _____
2. 8 plus 7 minus 6 _____
3. 5 plus 9 minus 6 _____
4. 11 minus 6 plus 9 minus 1 _____
5. 4 plus 8 plus 2 minus 7 _____

CHAPTER 6
1. 30 plus 20 _____
2. 46 plus 10 _____
3. 30 plus 22 plus 11 _____
4. 40 plus 10 plus 20 _____
5. 31 plus 9 plus 50 _____
6. 4 plus 6 plus 32 _____

CHAPTER 2   Following Directions
Use after textbook pages 31–32.   Page 1

Tell the class that you will give them directions for each problem.
They will listen carefully to know what to do.

1. If the larger number is in the circle, put an X on it. If the larger
   number is in the square, draw a ring around it.

2. If the larger number is on top, put an X on it. If the larger number
   is on the bottom, put a line under it.

3. If there are 6 flowers, draw a line under them. If there are 5 birds,
   draw some birdseed for them.

4. If there are 10 letters, draw a line around the Q. If there are 9
   numbers, draw a ring around the last number.

5. If the box has the larger sum, put the letter *M* under it. If the
   triangle has the larger sum, draw a ring around it.

6. If there are 11 grapes in the bunch, put the letter *O* under
   the grapes.

   If there are 9 apples in the pile, put the letter *C* under them.

CHAPTER 2   Writing Numbers
Use after textbook pages 39–40.   Page 2
Tell the class that you are going to read them a story. Tell them to listen carefully for numbers in the story. They will write the numbers they hear on their pages.

5 alligators swam to the Swampy Restaurant for dinner. Gertrude Gator ordered for everyone after they had looked at the menu. She said, "We would like 4 bowls of Special Swampy Stew, and 1 cup of mushroom soup. For our main course, we will have 6 lb of smashed potatoes and 18 fried crawdaddies. We would each like 3 tomatoes. That will be 15 tomatoes in all. Could we please have 28 purple radishes on the side. Gerry would like 1 glass of milk, Kate will have 2 glasses of cider, and we will need 3 glasses of Swamp Tea. For dessert, we will have 30 watermelon slices and 200 peeled grapes." After dinner, the alligators each paid $7.46 for their meal. They left the waiter a tip of $3.20. The alligators decided to walk home from dinner, as they were too full to swim.

CHAPTER 2   Following Directions
Use after textbook pages 43–44.   No student page.
Tell students that they will follow instructions that you will give them. They should pay special attention to the numbers they hear. Tell students that they will not be writing anything down. All students in the class will do the activities at the same time.

Activity 1—Give these directions to students.

- Stand up.
- Clap 4 times.
- Turn around 3 times.
- Tap head with right hand 5 times.
- Tap head with left hand 2 times.
- Tap shoulders 8 times.
- Jump 3 times.
- Hold up 8 fingers.
- Put down 5 fingers.
- Hold up 4 more fingers.
- Take away 6 fingers.
- Take away 1 finger.
- Put hands down.
- Turn around 2 times.
- Clap 5 times.
- Sit down.

Activity 2—Give these directions to students.

- Take 5 books out of the desk.
- Stack 5 books in a pile.
- Take away 3 books.
- Add 1 book to the pile.
- Add 2 books to the pile.
- Take away the math book.
- Open the math book to page 67.
- Turn back 6 pages. What page is it? *pg. 61*
- Turn forward 9 pages.
- Turn forward 5 more pages.
- Turn back 3 pages. What page are you on? *pg. 72*

Activity 3—Give these directions to students.

- Count the students in the class.
- Take away the number of windows in the classroom.
- Add the number of doors in the classroom.
- Take away 10 children in the class.
- Say the number out loud.

CHAPTER 3   Writing Corrected Answers
Use after textbook pages 77–78.   Page 3

Tell the class that you will read a story and question one time. Tell them to listen carefully to all of the information. They will write the answer on their page. Tell them that you will then read the story again. Ask the class to correct their answers if they need to.

Jack collects all sorts of funny things. He collects comic books. On Tuesday, he bought 3 *Cats in Space* comic books, 4 *Bitty the Detective Dog* comic books, and 2 *Monkey Business* comic books.

1. How many comic books does Jack buy? _____

Jack has collected 9 marbles. Julia gives him 5 marbles. He wins another 3 marbles from Billy. Jack keeps all of the marbles in a shoebox.

2. How many marbles are in the box? _____

In the autumn, Jack bicycles into the park to collect colored leaves. He gathers 6 elm leaves, 8 beech leaves, and 2 maple leaves.

3. In all, how many leaves does Jack collect? _____

Jack collects shoelaces. He has 7 pairs of bright yellow shoelaces, 5 pairs of plaid shoelaces, and 3 pairs of shoelaces with green polka dots.

4. How many pairs of shoelaces does Jack have altogether?
_____

Jack gave his sister Morgan 3 different whistles for her birthday one year. The next year, he gave her 6 more whistles.

5. How many whistles does Morgan have in all? _____

CHAPTER 4   Choosing the Correct Question
Use after textbook pages 93–94.   Page 4
Tell the class that you will read a problem two times. Tell them to listen to all of the information. You will ask them two questions. They will have to decide which question they can answer from the information given in the problem. Then they will answer the question next to the correct letter.

1. All of the robots on the Planet Zep like to play team sports. Fee, Fie, and Foe play on the same soccer team. Fee scored 9 goals this season, Fie only scored 5, and Foe scored the most.
    a. How many more goals did Fee score than Fie?
    b. How many goals did all three score?
2. Klim, Klop, and Fum play on the Bip baseball team. In one game, Klim gets 6 hits, Klop gets 9 hits, and Fum gets 2 hits.
    a. How many players are on the Bip baseball team?
    b. In all, how many hits did the three robots get in one game?
3. Lib and Lob played together in the Ping-Pong tournament. They played for 49 minutes in all. Plink and Plonk played for 57 minutes in all.
    a. Who played the most games?
    b. How many minutes did Plink and Plonk play?
4. Last year, the Zeps won 6 volleyball games. The Togos won 8 games. The Surfs played 14 volleyball games. They won 3 games.
    a. How many games did the Surfs lose?
    b. How many games did the Togos lose?
5. Blip, Flip, and Dip all play basketball. Blip has played for 2 years. Flip has played for 3 years. Dip has played for 5 years.
    a. How many games did Blip, Flip, and Dip play this year?
    b. How many years have Blip, Flip, and Dip played basketball?

CHAPTER 6   Find the Answer
Use after textbook pages 147–148.   Page 5
Tell the class to write the numbers 1 through 20 on the dog bones.
Then ask them to cut out the bones along the dotted lines so they will
each have twenty bones. Have students place the bones in numerical
order on their desks. Tell them that Spot, the puppy at the top of the
page, is very hungry. Ask them to listen to each number sentence and
find the bone that shows the correct answer. Then tell students that
they are to place the bone with the answer on it in Spot's bowl.

7 − 6 = _____	12 − 6 = _____	6 + 5 = _____	11 + 5 = _____
16 − 5 = _____	5 + 1 = _____	20 − 9 = _____	19 − 3 = _____
8 − 6 = _____	13 − 6 = _____	3 + 9 = _____	12 + 5 = _____
18 − 6 = _____	3 + 4 = _____	18 − 6 = _____	9 + 8 = _____
11 − 8 = _____	17 − 9 = _____	4 + 9 = _____	16 + 2 = _____
1 + 2 = _____	16 − 8 = _____	7 + 6 = _____	9 + 9 = _____
8 − 4 = _____	5 + 4 = _____	12 + 2 = _____	20 − 1 = _____
16 − 12 = _____	15 − 6 = _____	7 + 7 = _____	10 + 9 = _____
8 − 3 = _____	1 + 9 = _____	17 − 2 = _____	23 − 3 = _____
13 − 8 = _____	6 + 4 = _____	20 − 5 = _____	16 + 4 = _____

CHAPTER 6   Writing Questions
Use after textbook pages 155–156.   Page 6

Tell the class that you will read a story with numbers two times. Tell them to listen carefully to all the information given. Tell them to write the numbers in the story next to the thing they describe. After you read the story a second time, they will write a question with the numbers, using any information from the story. Then they will answer the question.

Mr. Zip has been delivering the mail for seven years. Everyone likes Mr. Zip because he is very friendly and dependable. Mrs. Wilson watches for Mr. Zip and invites him to see her garden. She is growing 3 marigolds and 5 petunias. Mr. Smith is also on Mr. Zip's route. He has 6 dogs and 4 cats. Mr. Zip tries to be quiet when he delivers the mail. If the dogs hear him, they begin to bark and this makes Mr. Zip nervous. Ms. Jones works at home and receives a lot of mail. She receives 7 letters and 5 bills each day. Mr. Zip loves his job. He is always there to deliver the mail, no matter what the weather—rain, snow, hail, or sleet.

CHAPTER 6   Numbers in a Poem
Use after textbook pages 157–158.   Page 7

Tell the class that you will read each verse of the poem twice, and ask a question about it. Ask them to listen for the important numbers. The second time you read the question, the class is to answer it on their papers.

Forty-five elephants rode the train
From Kalamazoo to Portland, Maine.
Then four more elephants climbed on board.
The train whistle blew and the engine roared.

How many elephants were on the train in all?

_____ elephants

Twenty miles of countryside rolled right by.
Then nineteen miles more in the blink of an eye.
The elephants waved to the people outside.
"Great fun," they said. "This is quite a ride."

How many miles did the train travel? _____ miles

At one o'clock the train started up a hill.
It groaned and moaned and spluttered until,
At 2 o'clock, it came to a stop.
Then strong elephants pushed it over the top.

At what time did the train start up the hill? _____ o'clock

The elephants traveled from shore to shore.
They visited the Capitol and Mount Rushmore.
After 21 days of roaming in a train,
They spent 5 more days riding home again.

How many days in all did the elephants spend traveling?

_____ days

CHAPTER 6   Choose the Right Numbers
Use after textbook pages 161–162.   Page 8

Tell the class that you are going to read them a story twice. You will stop in the middle of the story and ask them questions about what they have heard. Tell them to listen for the numbers they need, and the numbers they don't need. Tell them that you will read the question at the end of each section twice. Then they will answer the questions on their page.

Rufus Raccoon is having a party on April 6 for his friend Otis Owl. Rufus invites 8 owls from the forest, including Otis. He also invites 5 foxes and 4 deer.

1. How many owls and foxes are invited to the party in all?

_____

Eggy Owl will take invitations to the deer and foxes. She flies 4 miles to the hollow where the deer live. On the way, Eggy sees 6 frogs. Then she flies 9 miles to the cave where the foxes live.

2. How many miles does Eggy fly? _____

Rufus asks the Bird Choir to sing at the party. There are 17 birds in the choir. Nine of the birds live next door to Rufus. Only 11 of the birds will be able to sing at the party.

3. How many birds in the choir will not be able to sing at the party?

_____

Rufus plans the food he will serve. He fixes one forest salad for each of the deer. Rufus counts out 7 berries, 10 lettuce leaves, and 11 hazelnuts for each salad. He also squeezes one glass of carrot juice for each deer.

4. How many berries and nuts are in each forest salad? _____

On the day of the party, Rufus blows up 18 balloons. He strings 44 colored lights around the trees. When the birds arrive, they bring 13 more balloons.

5. How many balloons are there at the party? _____

CHAPTER 7   Writing the Number
Use after textbook pages 183–184.   Page 9

Tell the class that you are going to read them a story twice. The first time, they need to listen carefully for the numbers they need and the numbers they don't need. Tell them that you will stop during the story and ask questions about what they have heard. Tell the class that the second time you read the story, they will write down the numbers they need and the numbers they don't need. Tell them you will read the questions at the end of each section twice, and that they should write the answers to the questions on their page.

Pat and Ken can't wait for Fun Land Amusement Park to open for the summer. The park has added 5 new exciting rides during the winter. One of the new rides is a scarey roller coaster. Last year the amusement park had 20 rides.

1. How many rides does Fun Land Amusement Park have this summer? _____

Tomorrow is the big day. Pat and Ken will get up at 7 A.M. Mother promised they would leave at 9 A.M., and it takes 1 hour to drive to Fun Land.

2. How much time will Pat and Ken have to eat breakfast and clean their rooms before they leave for Fun Land? _____

When they arrive at Fun Land, the first ride that Pat and Ken see is the river-boat ride. Last year, it cost 15¢ a ride. This year, one ride costs 20¢. Ken and Pat each ride it twice and then go to the roller coaster.

3. How much money did Ken and Pat spend for the boat rides? _____

Pat and Ken decide that the line for the new roller coaster is too long. So, they both walk through the fun house which costs 50¢. Pat gives the girl in the ticket booth a $1 bill to pay for their tickets.

4. How much change did she receive? _____

Ken is getting hungry. He wants some raisins, which cost 35¢, and a glass of apple juice, which costs 40¢. He has 3 quarters and a dime in coins and a $1 bill in his pocket.

5. Does he have enough coins to pay for his food? _____

By the end of the afternoon, Pat and Ken are tired, but they have had a great day. Pat has 2 quarters left and Ken has $1. Before they go home, Pat wants to buy a Fun Land poster and a giant Fun Land pencil as souvenirs. The poster costs 35¢ and the pencil costs 20¢.

6. Does she have enough money to buy both souvenirs? _____

LISTENING AND WRITING MATH

CHAPTERS 7–12 Speed Drill
Use after each textbook chapter.   No student page.
These speed drills can be used with the last six chapters to improve
students' listening skills. Tell students that you will read each
problem two times. They will write the answer to the problem on a
separate sheet of paper.

CHAPTER 7
1. 43 minus 20 _____

2. 68 minus 48 _____

3. 50 plus 3 minus 40 _____

4. 27 plus 3 minus 10 _____

5. 34 plus 6 minus 15 _____

6. 55 plus 5 minus 50 _____

CHAPTER 10
1. One more than 125 _____

2. One less than 865 _____

3. The number between 439 and 441 _____

4. The number between 398 and 400 _____

5. One more than 200 _____

6. One less than 670 _____

CHAPTER 11
1. 501 plus 204 _____

2. 620 plus 300 _____

3. $2.00 + $4.00 _____

4. $0.50 ± $3.50 minus $2.00 _____

5. 100 plus 218 minus 218 _____

6. 700 minus 400 plus 600 minus 500 _____

CHAPTER 12
1. 2 plus 5 times 4 _____

2. 3 times 3 plus 30 _____

3. 17 minus 10 times 5 _____

4. 3 times 1 plus 17 _____

5. 8 times 4 plus 3 _____

6. 4 times 5 minus 5 _____

7. 2 plus 7 times 3 _____

CHAPTER 9   Map Directions
Use after textbook pages 243–244.   Page 10

Tell the class to look at the picture of the toys in the window of the Singing Yoyo Toy Store. Tell them you will read each direction twice. They will start at the amount of $1.26 and draw a straight line to each toy that costs the amount of money you read. They will see something special if they trace the paths correctly.

1. Start at $1.26. Draw a straight line from $1.26 to the toy that you can buy with a dime and a nickel.
2. From there, draw a straight line to the toy that you can buy with 4 dimes, a nickel, and a penny.
3. From there, draw a straight line to the toy that you can buy with 2 quarters and 1 dollar bill.
4. From there, draw a straight line to the toy that you can buy with 2 dimes.
5. From there, draw a straight line to the toy that you can buy with one dollar, a quarter, and a penny.

CHAPTER 10   Numbers from a News Story
Use after textbook pages 271–272.   Page 11

Numbers are everywhere. We hear them on television and the radio. We see them in the newspaper, on buildings, in restaurants, and in movie theaters. Tell the class that you will read a story that appeared in the newspaper. They are to listen carefully and write down all the numbers that they hear in the story.

Today, 4 children in the Midwest were rewarded for their honesty. They shared the 5 bags of money that they had found on a stream bank. Mike, age 13; Julie, age 10; Theresa, age 11; and Justin, age 8, found the money as they were watching frogs in the stream. Mike first stepped on a bag that was full of coins.

"We opened the bag and counted 250 quarters. Then we began to look for more," Mike said. Julie found another bag that had 120 coins. Each coin was worth 50¢. Justin found a bag that had 400 dimes. Theresa found 2 more bags full of coins and bills. The children brought the money to the police station. The police chief said that they had done the right thing. If no one claimed the money in 6 months, the money would be returned to the children.

Today, the children collected the money from the police station. The chief thanked them for their honesty. Theresa said they would give some of the money to the city food pantry. Mike and Julie decided they would buy 2 bicycles. Justin said he would buy 1 videocassette recorder for his family. Theresa said she would also spend some money on a trip to California 9 months from now.

CHAPTER 11   Giving Directions

Use work sheet 12 after pages 293–294.   Pages 12, 13, and 14.
Use work sheet 13 after pages 293–294.
Use work sheet 14 after pages 295–296.

Tell students that they are to work in groups of two. Student A will take the work sheet. Student B will have a blank sheet of paper. Student A will describe the picture on the work sheet to Student B. The object is for Student B to draw the picture as Student A describes it.

Both students will need a ruler. Student A should measure the length of the lines before they begin.

Student A should give exact directions and try to make the instructions as clear and easy as possible. The type of instructions should be something like this:

1. Draw a square in the center of your paper. Each side of the square is 3 inches long.
2. Draw a rectangle on top of the square. The long side is 2 inches long. The short side is 1 inch long. Draw the rectangle so the short side is next to the top of the square. Try to put the rectangle in the middle of the square.

CHAPTER 17   Three-Minute Test

Use after textbook pages 313–314.   Page 15

Give each of the students a copy of the test. Tell them to keep the test facedown until you tell them to begin. Tell the class to read all the instructions before they do anything. They will have 3 minutes to do the test.

CHAPTER 12   Writing Problems
Use after textbook pages 323–324.   Page 15

Tell the class that you will read part of a story two times. Tell them to listen for all the numbers and information given. Tell them you will not ask any questions. They will write the operations they would use to make a problem out of the story using +, −, and ×. Then they will write a problem and answer it.

1. Pia and her mother go to buy house plants. Pia likes the African violet. It costs $1.25. Her mother likes the ivy, which costs $1.31. Their house has lots of sunny windows for plants.

2. There are 4 houses on Jerry's street. Jerry's house is one of them. Saturday, everyone raked leaves. They put the leaves in large garbage bags. Each house had 3 bags of leaves. On Monday, the garbage truck picked up the bags.

3. Ellen and Brad want to grow vegetables on the roof of their apartment building. Ellen plants 4 tomato plants in a flower box. Brad plants 5 squash plants in a round tub. They water their roof-top garden every day.

4. Maria buys some tools for working in her roof-top flower garden. A watering can costs $1.50. A shovel costs $4.25. She cares for the flowers every morning.

5. Becky wants to plant a garden in her backyard. She buys a pack of carrot seeds, one pack of lettuce seeds, and one pack of bean seeds. Each pack costs 10¢.

LISTENING AND WRITING MATH   **Following Directions**

When you hear the information:
- Listen to the directions.
- Do what you are asked.

 1.

2.

3.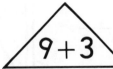

4. A C E F H M
    N Q S U X Z

    2 4 6 8 10
    12 14 16 18

5.

6.

LISTENING AND WRITING MATH

Writing Numbers

When you hear the information:
• Listen for the numbers in the story.
• Write the numbers as you hear them.

_____

_____

_____

_____

_____

_____

_____

_____

_____

_____

_____

_____

LISTENING AND WRITING MATH | Writing Corrected Answers

When you hear the information:
- Listen to all of the information.
- Write your answer.
- Listen to the story again.
- Correct your answer.

1. Answer: _____

 Corrected answer: _____

2. Answer: _____

 Corrected answer: _____

3. Answer: _____

 Corrected answer: _____

4. Answer: _____

 Corrected answer: _____

5. Answer: _____

 Corrected answer: _____

LISTENING AND WRITING MATH

Choosing the Correct Question

When you hear the information:
- Listen for the numbers and information.
- Choose the correct question.
- Answer the question.

1. a. _____

   b. _____

2. a. _____

   b. _____

3. a. _____

   b. _____

4. a. _____

   b. _____

5. a. _____

   b. _____

LISTENING AND WRITING MATH

Find the Answer

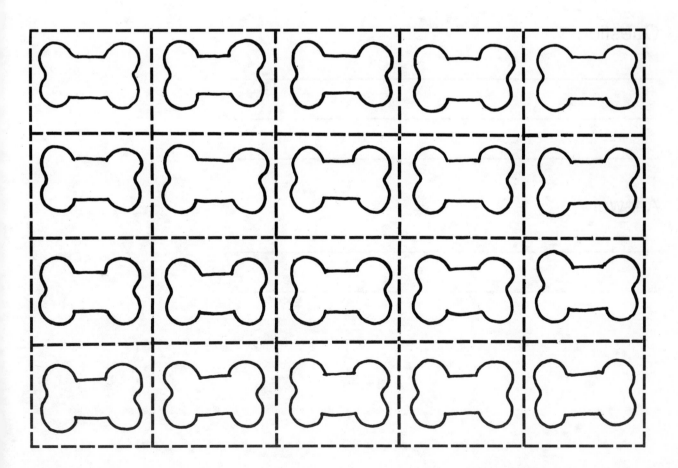

LISTENING AND WRITING MATH
Writing Questions

When you hear the information:
- Listen for the numbers in the story.
- Write a question using numbers and information from the story.

flowers _____

dogs _____

cats _____

letters _____

bills _____

Question

_____

_____

_____

Answer

_____

_____

LISTENING AND WRITING MATH Numbers in a Poem

When you hear the information:
- Listen for the important numbers.
- Write the answer.

1. Answer: _____

2. Answer: _____

3. Answer: _____

4. Answer: _____

LISTENING AND WRITING MATH

Choose the Right Numbers

When you hear the information:
- Listen for the numbers you need.
- Listen for the numbers you don't need.

1. What numbers do you need? _____

   What numbers don't you need? _____

   Answer: _____

2. What numbers do you need? _____

   What numbers don't you need? _____

   Answer: _____

3. What numbers do you need? _____

   What numbers don't you need? _____

   Answer: _____

4. What numbers do you need? _____

   What numbers don't you need? _____

   Answer: _____

5. What numbers do you need? _____

   What numbers don't you need? _____

   Answer: _____

LISTENING AND WRITING MATH

Writing the Number

When you hear the information:
- Listen for the numbers you need.
- Listen for the numbers you don't need.

1. What numbers do you need?

_____

What numbers don't you need?

_____

Answer: _____

2. What numbers do you need?

_____

What numbers don't you need?

_____

Answer: _____

3. What numbers do you need?

_____

What numbers don't you need?

_____

Answer: _____

4. What numbers do you need?

_____

What numbers don't you need?

_____

Answer: _____

5. What numbers do you need?

_____

What numbers don't you need?

_____

Answer: _____

6. What numbers do you need?

_____

What numbers don't you need?

_____

Answer: _____

LISTENING AND WRITING MATH

Map Directions

When you hear the information:
* Listen for the amount of
  money given. • Follow the directions.

THE SINGING YOYO TOY STORE

20¢

$2.28

$1.40

15¢

62¢

46¢

54¢

$1.50

$1.26

LISTENING AND WRITING MATH

Numbers from a News Story

When you hear the information:
- Listen for numbers in the news story.
- Write the numbers as you hear them.

_____

_____

_____

_____

_____

_____

_____

_____

_____

_____

_____

_____

LISTENING AND WRITING MATH
Giving Directions

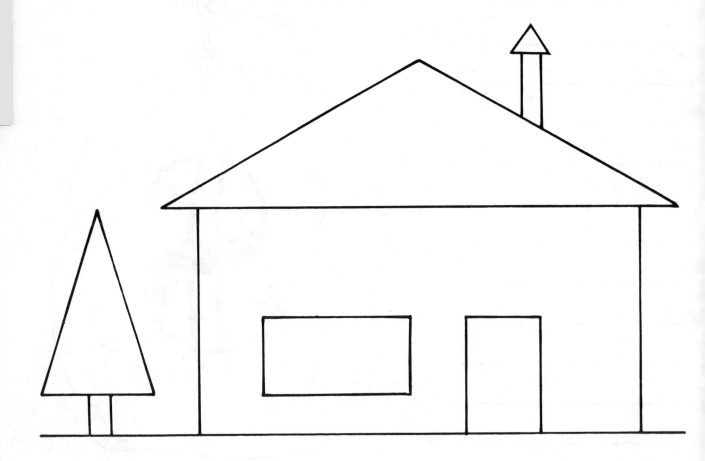

Use after pages 293–294.

LISTENING AND WRITING MATH Giving Directions

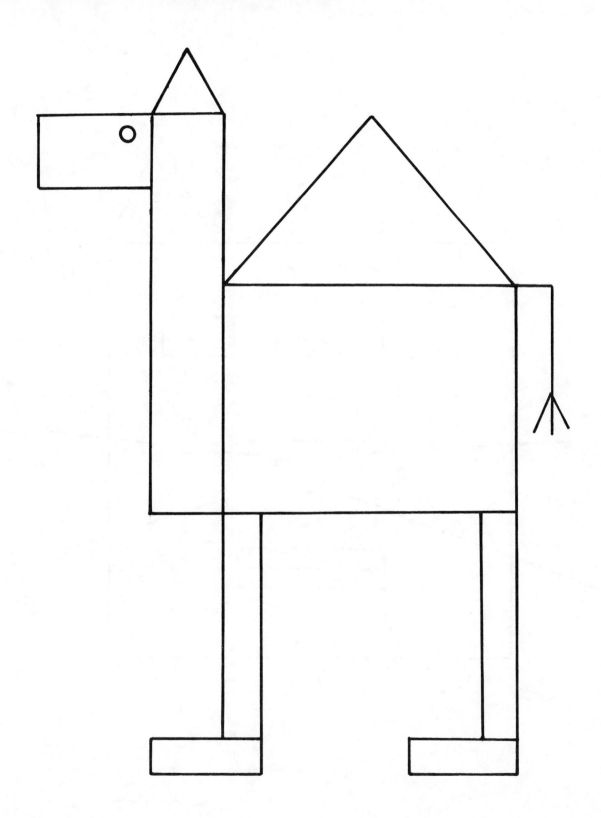

Name _____ Date _____

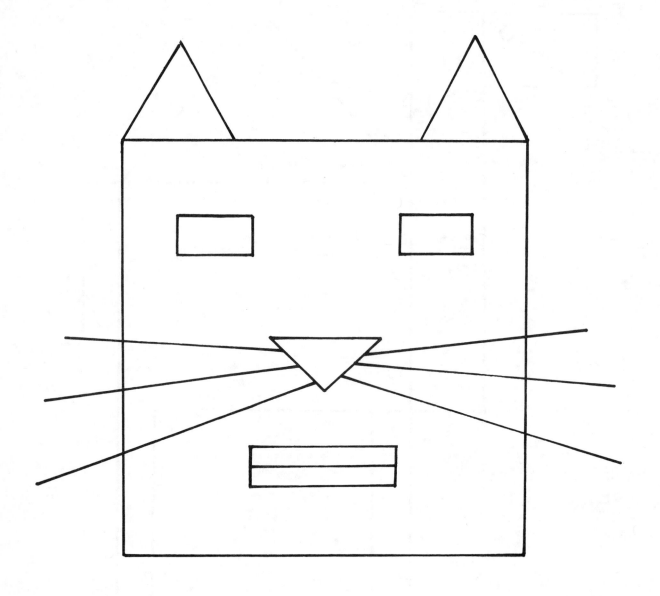

Name _____ Date _____

1. Circle your first name.

2. Add 3 + 5. Write the answer on the back of this page.

3. Draw a square under the date.

4. Draw a triangle under the square.

5. Clap your hands 3 times fast and 6 times slowly.

6. On the back of this page, multiply 4 × 6.

7. Write "I will finish this test first" 5 times on the back of this paper.

8. Find 346 − 28. Write your answer on the bottom of this page.

9. Now that you have read the whole test, don't do anything.

LISTENING AND WRITING MATH   Writing Problems

- Listen to all of the information.
- Write $+$, $-$, or $\times$.
- Write your problem.
- Answer your question.

1. What do you do? _____

   Answer: _____

2. What do you do? _____

   Answer: _____

3. What do you do? _____

   Answer: _____

4. What do you do? _____

   Answer: _____

5. What do you do? _____

   Answer: _____

no student page

Chapter 1:
1. 4
2. 8
3. 7
4. 9
5. 12
6. 6

Chapter 2:
1. 22
2. 54
3. 62
4. 87
5. 30

Chapter 3:
1. 16
2. 9
3. 14
4. 16
5. 15

Chapter 4:
1. 7
2. 9
3. 8
4. 13
5. 7

Chapter 6:
1. 50
2. 56
3. 63
4. 70
5. 90
6. 42

Page 1

1. ring around square
2. X on 8
3. line under flowers
4. ring around the last number
5. ring around the triangle
6. C under the apples

Page 2

Check children's lists of numbers.
5
4
1
6
18
3
15
28
1
2
3
30

Page 2 (cont'd.)

200
$7.46
$3.20

no student page
Make sure that children perform activities accurately, according to directions.

Page 3

1. 9 **2.** 17 **3.** 16 **4.** 15 **5.** 9

Page 4

1. a; 4
2. b; 17
3. b; 57
4. a; 11
5. b; 10

Page 5

Row 1: 1, 6, 11, 16
Row 2: 11, 6, 11, 16
Row 3: 2, 7, 12, 17
Row 4: 12, 7, 12, 17
Row 5: 3, 8, 13, 18
Row 6: 3, 8, 13, 18
Row 7: 4, 9, 14, 19
Row 8: 4, 9, 14, 19
Row 9: 5, 10, 15, 20
Row 10: 5, 10, 15, 20

Page 6

3 marigolds
5 petunias
6 dogs
4 cats
7 letters
5 bills
Children will use this information to write questions of their own. Check children's answers to these questions.

Page 7

1. 49 elephants
2. 39 miles
3. 1 o'clock
4. 26 days

Page 8

1. 13 owls and foxes
2. 13 miles

Page 8 (cont'd.)

3. 6 birds
4. 18 berries and nuts
5. 31 balloons

Page 9

1. 25 rides
2. 2 hours
3. 80¢
4. 0
5. yes
6. no

no student page
Chapter 7:
1. 23
2. 20
3. 13
4. 20
5. 25
6. 10

Chapter 10:
1. 126
2. 864
3. 440
4. 399
5. 201
6. 669

Chapter 11:
1. 705
2. 920
3. $6.00
4. $2.00
5. 100
6. 400

Chapter 12:
1. 28
2. 39
3. 35
4. 20
5. 35
6. 15
7. 27

Page 10

1. Connect $1.26 with 15¢.
2. Connect 15¢ with 46¢.
3. Connect 46¢ with $1.50.
4. Connect $1.50 with 20¢.
5. Connect 20¢ with $1.26.
The lines drawn form a star.

LISTENING AND WRITING MATH ANSWER KEY

Page 11

Check children's lists of numbers.
4
5
13
10
11
8
250
120
50¢
400
2
6
2
1
9

Page 12

Check to be sure that children measure accurately and then give and follow precise directions.

Page 13

Check to be sure that children measure accurately and then give and follow precise directions.

Page 14

Check to be sure that children measure accurately and then give and follow precise directions.

Page 15

After children have, correctly, read all test instructions, they should sit quietly, doing nothing. They will be following the final instruction on the test.

Page 16

Answers will vary on all problems.

MATH RELAYS   Addend Runaround

Number of Players
- Teams of five or six
- A leader

What You Need
- Index cards
- Pencil

How to Play

1. Each player numbers his or her cards from 0 to 9.
2. The leader places his or her cards facedown in a pile.
3. The leader picks a card and shows it to the teams.
4. Players on each team must find all of the addends that equal the number on the card held by the leader.
5. The first team to find all of the addends from their pile of cards scores 1 point.
6. Play continues with the leader picking another card from his or her pile and showing it to the team.
7. The first team to score 12 points wins.

MATH RELAYS   Fishing for Facts

Number of Players
- Teams of six

What You Need
- Scissors
- Unsharpened pencil for each team
- 10-inch piece of string for each team
- Jumbo paper clip for each team
- Hole punch
- Crayon

How to Play
1. Each team makes one fishing pole.
   Bend the clip to make a hook like this: 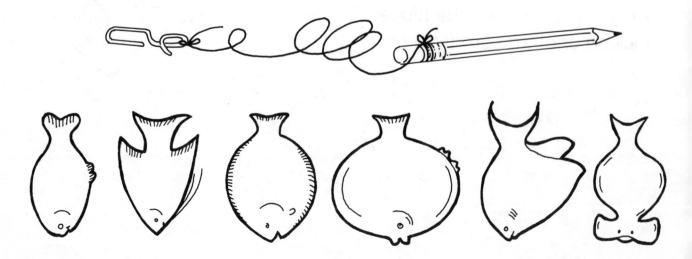 .
   Tie one end of the string to the hook and the other end to the pencil.

2. Color and cut out the fish. Write an addition or subtraction fact from 7 to 12 on each one.
   Punch a hole in each to make a mouth.
3. Each team places all six players' fish on a table edge so that their mouths can be "hooked." You're ready to go!
4. Assign each player on each team a number from 7 to 12.
5. Players from each team take turns fishing for a fact that equals his or her number.
6. The team that has the most fish at the end of fifteen minutes wins.

MATH RELAYS — Payday Relay

Number of Players
- Teams of three, six or nine
- A leader

What You Need
- Chalkboard
- Chalk
- Scissors
- Paper

How to Play
1. Cut out the money cards. Place them facedown in two equal stacks on the leader's desk.
2. The leader writes *Tens Bank* on one side of the chalkboard, and *Ones Bank* on the other side.
3. When the leader says "Go," Player 1 from each team picks a card from the stack.
4. Player 1 from each team reads the amount on the card and runs first to the Tens Bank.
5. Each player writes down the number of tens.
6. Then the players run to the Ones Bank and write down the number of ones. Then it's back to the leader's desk.
7. The first player to correctly "cash in" the card with the leader earns 1 point for his or her team.
8. The leader records the points. The first team that has 10 points wins.

$70	$18	$42	$53	$4	$26	$75	$67	$48
$96	$60	$71	$12	$33	$84	$55	$91	$23

MATH RELAYS   More or Less Marathon

Number of Players
- Teams of any number
- A leader

What You Need
- 15 index cards
- Black ink marker
- Scissors

How to Play
1. Each team cuts out one set of number cards and places a set of cards on a table faceup in front of the team.
2. The leader writes a 2-digit number on each index card.
3. Player 1 sits in front of his or her team cards with hands folded.

4. The leader holds up an index card and calls "One More!" or "One Less!"
5. Players must find the pair of cards that show the number that is 1 more or 1 less.
6. The player who shows the correct pair of cards first earns 1 point for the team.
7. Play continues until everyone has had at least one chance to play.
8. The team that has the most points wins.

Score Card	
Team 1	**Team 2**

1	2	3	4	5	6	7	8	9	0

MATH RELAYS   **Run for the Numbers**

Number of Players
- Teams of eight
- A leader

What You Need
- Chalkboard
- Chalk for each team

How to Play
1. The leader writes *Team 1* on part of the chalkboard, *Team 2* on another part, and so on.
2. Each player on a team is given a number from 1 to 8.
3. Each team makes a straight line and faces the chalkboard in order from the least to the greatest number.

4. Teams stand about ten feet from the chalkboard.
5. The leader calls out an addition fact to 18, such as "six + five!"
6. The players assigned the numbers 6 and 5 on each team must go to the board and write the correct sum.
7. The pair of players who write the correct sum first earns a point for their team.
8. The first team to earn 18 points wins.

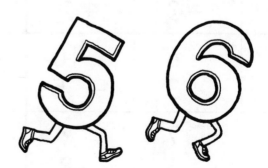

MATH RELAYS **Crackerjack Facts**

Number of Players
- Two teams of any number
- A leader

What You Need
- 24 plastic coins
- Large boxtop (20-in. by 20-in.)
- Black ink marker
- Ruler

How to Play
1. The leader copies the fact board as shown onto a large boxtop to form a grid of fact squares.
2. Player 1 from Team 1 stands four feet from the fact board and tosses a coin onto the board.

3. If the coin lands on a line, the player must answer the fact nearest to the coin. If the player answers correctly, the player keeps the coin. If the answer is incorrect, the coin is left on the fact-board square.
4. If the coin lands on the square and the player answers correctly, the player takes all of the coins on the board.
5. Player 1 from Team 2 takes a turn.
6. The team that has the most coins wins.

4 +8	5 −3	2 +2	6 +9	8 −1	0 +5
6 −2	6 +3	10 − 5	5 +8	4 +7	2 −2
8 +1	7 −6	8 +8	10 − 4	2 +1	4 +2
10 − 2	8 +2	6 −1	4 +7	6 +8	6 +1

MATH RELAYS   Time Out!

Number of Players
- Two teams with any number of players
- A leader

What You Need
- Chalkboard
- Chalk
- Pencil
- Scoresheet

How to Play
1. The leader draws a clock face on the left side of the chalkboard.
2. Each team lines up in a row fifteen feet from the chalkboard.
3. When the leader says "Go," Player 1 from Team 1 walks to the clock and draws two clock hands to show a time.

The Players use hour and half-hour examples only.

4. Player 1 from Team 2 writes that time in digital form on the right side of the chalkboard.
5. If Player 1 is correct, the leader gives Team 2 1 point on the scoresheet. If he or she is incorrect, the team does not earn a point.
6. The leader erases the hands and the time.
7. Player 2 from Team 2 draws the hands to show another time. Player 2 from Team 1 writes the time in digital form.
8. The first team to earn 12 points wins.

Scoresheet	
Team 1	**Team 2**

Use after pages 111–112.

MATH RELAYS Boomerang

Number of Players
- Two teams with any number of players
- A scorekeeper

What You Need
- Metric tape measure
- Thin cardboard
- Scissors
- Paper
- Pencil for each player

How to Play
1. Each player traces the boomerang onto the cardboard. He or she cuts out the boomerang and colors it.
2. Each team chooses a name for itself.
3. The scorekeeper folds a piece of paper in half and writes a team name at the top of each half.
4. Players flick their boomerang off a table corner by using their thumb and middle finger (see the picture).
5. The scorekeeper measures each shot and writes the distances on the scoresheet.
6. The team that has the longest shot after each player has had four turns wins.

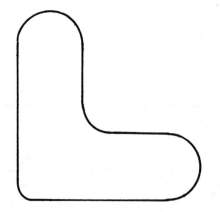
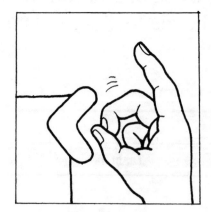

MATH RELAYS Add Them Up

Number of Players
- Teams of two or more

What You Need
- 16 index cards for each team
- Different-colored crayon for each player on a team
- Game board per player

How to Play
1. Each team writes any number from 5 to 50 on each index card.
2. Put all the cards for a team facedown in a pile on a desk.
3. Player 1 chooses two cards and adds their numbers.

4. If the sum matches a number on the game board, Player 1 crosses out that sum on his or her game board.
5. After each turn, the player puts his or her cards at the bottom of the pile.
6. Play continues until a player has crossed out five numbers to win.
7. To play again, draw a game board on another piece of paper.

85	32	59	25
50	18	63	67
96	74	36	49

Holt, Rinehart and Winston, Publishers • 2

MATH RELAYS **Regroup!**

Number of Players
- Two teams with any number of players
- A leader

What You Need
- 50 index cards
- Felt-tip pen
- Scoresheet per game

How to Play

1. The leader writes one digit from 0 to 9 on each card. There must be five cards of each digit.
2. The leader shuffles the cards and places them facedown in a pile on a table.
3. Each team lines up in front of the leader.
4. The leader shows the top two cards to the first player from each team.

5. The players must add the digits together. If the sum is 9 or less, the player calls out the sum. If the sum is greater than 9, the player says how many ones are left after regrouping and then calls out "Regroup!"
6. The first player to answer correctly scores a point for his or her team. The leader marks the point on the scoresheet.
7. The cards are placed at the bottom of the pile, and Player 1 from each team goes to the end of their line.
8. Play continuing until a team earns 10 points.

Scorsheet	
Team 1	**Team 2**

MATH RELAYS Take Away Toss-up

Number of Players
- Two teams with any number of players
- A leader

What You Need
- 99 chips in a box
- Timer

How to Play
1. The leader arranges the ninety-nine chips on a table in rows of ten. The last row has nine.
2. The teams line up facing each other with the chips between them.
3. The leader says "Go," and starts the timer for fifteen minutes.
4. Player I from Team I says "ninety-nine," and takes away one to nine chips. Player I says how many he or she took and puts them into the box. Player I walks to the end of the line.
5. Player I from Team 2 must say how many chips are left on the table.
6. If the player is correct, the leader gives that team a point, and says "Go."
7. If a player says the wrong difference, the leader says "Toss-up!" The first player to say the right difference scores 5 points for their team.
8. Player 2 from Team 2 then takes away chips. Player 2 from Team I must now say the difference.
9. The team that has the most points after fifteen minutes wins.

MATH RELAYS **Shape-Up Marathon**

Number of Players
- Two teams with any number of players

What You Need
- Scissors
- 2 paper bags

How to Play
1. Each team cuts out a set of shape cards and puts them facedown on the table.
2. The teams sit facing each other with the table between them.
3. Player 1 in Team 1 takes a shape card. The players on Team 2 take turns asking questions about the shape; for example: "Does it have 3 corners?" The answers must be either *yes* or *no.*
4. If Team 2 can guess the shape in five turns, the shape card goes in Team 2's bag. If Team 2 cannot guess the shape in five turns, the shape card goes in Team 1's bag.
5. Teams take turns picking cards and guessing shapes.
6. After all the cards are used, the team that has the most cards in its bag wins the game.

CIRCLE	TRIANGLE	SQUARE	RECTANGLE	SPHERE	CYLINDER	CUBE	CONE	RECTANGULAR PRISM

MATH RELAYS   Fraction Action

Number of Players
- Teams of five or more
- A leader

What You Need
- Index cards
- Pen
- Scissors
- Glue

How to Play

1. The leader cuts out the cards below and glues one card on each index card. He or she puts them facedown on a table.

2. Each player on a team is assigned a different fraction:

Each player writes his or her fraction on an index card.

$$\frac{1}{2}, \frac{1}{4}, \frac{3}{4}, \frac{1}{8}, \frac{6}{8}, \frac{1}{3}, \frac{2}{3}, \text{ or } \frac{1}{6}.$$

3. Player 1 on Team 1 picks a card from the table. If the card matches Player 1's fraction, Team 1 keeps the card. If the card does not match, it must be returned to the table facedown at the bottom of the pile.

4. Then Player 1 from Team 2 picks a card, trying to match his or her fraction.

5. The first team to keep three cards wins a round. Play any number of rounds.

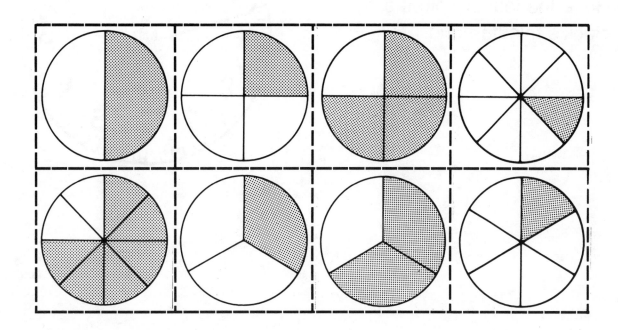

MATH RELAYS   **Clockworks**

Number of Players
- Two teams
- A leader

What You Need
- Cardboard
- Paper fastener
- Scissors
- Pencil

How to Play
1. Make one clock out of cardboard. Draw in the hour hand.
2. Draw and cut out a minute hand. Attach it to the clock with the paper fastener.
3. Line up teams in front of the clock.
4. Have the leader spin the clock's minute hand.

5. Player 1 on each team looks at the clock. The first one to raise his or her hand and correctly tell the time (to the nearest five minutes) scores 1 point for the team.
6. If the answer is incorrect, Player 1 from the other team can answer.
7. Play continues until each player has had one turn.
8. The team that has the most points wins.

MATH RELAYS Run A-weigh

Number of Players
- Teams of three to four
- A leader
- Timer

What You Need
- Postage scale
- Objects around classroom

How to Play
1. The leader calls out "Less than a pound."
2. Each team must find objects in the room that weigh less than a pound.
3. After three minutes, the leader weighs each object each team has found. Teams earn 1 point for each object that is less than one pound, and lose 1 point if the object is more than a pound.
4. The leader calls out "More than a pound," "More than half a pound," and then "Less than half a pound."
6. The team that has the most points wins.

MATH RELAYS Number Scramble

Number of Players
- Teams of two or more

What You Need
- Pencil for each player

How to Play
1. Each player on each team lists the numbers from the least to the greatest.
2. When all players on one team finish, everyone must stop.
3. One point is scored for each number that has been correctly ordered.
4. Each team adds up their points. The team that has the highest score wins.
5. Make up new numbers, scramble them, and play again.

NUMBER SHEET

Scrambled		In order
358	1.	
765	2.	
251	3.	
115	4.	
895	5.	
649	6.	
443	7.	
919	8.	
111	9.	
264	10.	
743	11.	
543	12.	

MATH RELAYS **Number Drill**

Number of Players
- Teams of two or more

What You Need
- Pencil for each player
- Gamesheet for each player

How to Play
1. Players race to complete all of the squares.
2. When the first player finishes, the game is over.
3. Players as a group check each other's answers.
4. Players total their scores by teams. The team that has the most points wins.

---

4 Points

Write the number that is 1 more and 1 less.

Less		More
____	775	____
____	856	____
____	321	____
____	433	____

---

4 Points

Less than or greater than?

114 ____ 211

456 ____ 371

783 ____ 941

123 ____ 650

---

4 Points

Read and write the number.

two hundred twenty-five ____

three hundred eleven ____

forty-six ____

MATH RELAYS Batter Up!

Number of Players
- Two teams of four or more
- A leader

What You Need
- Scrap paper
- Index cards
- Pencils
- Four bases

How to Play
1. The leader writes the problems on index cards.
2. The leader of Team 2 is up at bat. Team 1 takes the field and places the four bases around the classroom.
3. The leader of Team 1 asks Player 1 on Team 2 the first problem.
4. If the answer is correct, Player 1 goes to first base. If the answer is wrong, the player is out. Player 2 can try to correctly solve the problem.
5. As the team answers

correctly, the players move from base to base, until they reach home plate and score a run.
6. Teams switch when the team at bat has three outs.
7. The team that has the most runs at the end of five innings wins.
8. Add more problems to play again.

1.
$$\begin{array}{r} 382 \\ +192 \\ \hline 574 \end{array}$$

2.
$$\begin{array}{r} 247 \\ +\ 80 \\ \hline 327 \end{array}$$

3.
$$\begin{array}{r} 109 \\ +\ 87 \\ \hline 196 \end{array}$$

4.
$$\begin{array}{r} 268 \\ +160 \\ \hline 428 \end{array}$$

5.
$$\begin{array}{r} 333 \\ +157 \\ \hline 490 \end{array}$$

6.
$$\begin{array}{r} 526 \\ +380 \\ \hline 906 \end{array}$$

   Use after pages 301–302.

MATH RELAYS   Number Toss

Number of Players
- Teams of two or more

What You Need
- Six number cubes
- Pencil for each player
- Paper

How to Play
1. Player I rolls all six number cubes.
2. Add all the numbers that are on top.
3. Write that number on the scoresheet.
4. After ten rolls, the team that has the highest score wins.

Scoresheet	
Roll	Score
1	
2	
3	
4	
5	
6	
7	
8	
9	
10	
Total	

MATH RELAYS Math-a-Thon

Number of Players
- Teams of three to five
- A leader

What You Need
- Pencils
- Paper

How to Play
1. Each player uses the gamesheet to solve the multiplication problems.
2. Players must stop when one player has crossed the finish line.
3. Each correct problem is worth 1 point.
4. Players total their points. The player that has the most points wins the game.
5. On another piece of paper, make up a new maze and play again.

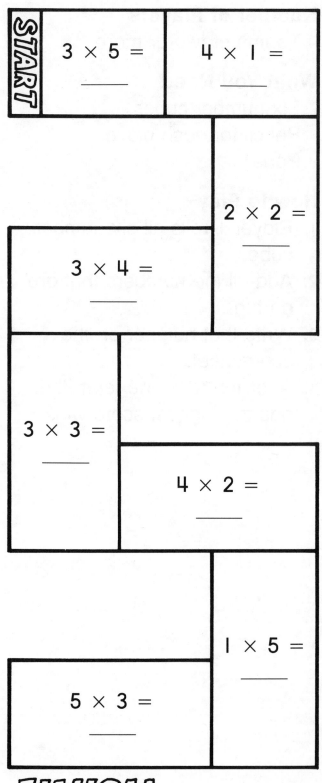

START

$3 \times 5 =$ _____

$4 \times 1 =$ _____

$2 \times 2 =$ _____

$3 \times 4 =$ _____

$3 \times 3 =$ _____

$4 \times 2 =$ _____

$1 \times 5 =$ _____

$5 \times 3 =$ _____

FINISH

MATH RELAYS ANSWER KEY

Page 1

Children will follow game rules as presented.

Page 2

Children will follow game rules as presented.

Page 3

Children will follow game rules as presented.

Page 4

Children will follow game rules as presented.

Page 5

Children will follow game rules as presented.

Page 6

Children will follow game rules as presented.

Page 7

Children will follow game rules as presented.

Page 8

Children will follow game rules as presented.

Page 9

Children will follow game rules as presented.

Page 10

Children will follow game rules as presented.

Page 11

Children will follow game rules as presented.

Page 12

Children will follow game rules as presented.

Page 13

Children will follow game rules as presented.

Page 14

Children will follow game rules as presented.

Page 15

Children will follow game rules as presented.

Page 16

1. 111 **2.** 115 **3.** 251 **4.** 264
5. 358 **6.** 443 **7.** 543 **8.** 649
9. 743 **10.** 765 **11.** 895
12. 919

Page 17

774; 776
855; 85
320; 322
432; 434
<
>
<
<
225
311
46

Page 18

Children will follow game rules as presented.

Page 19

Children will follow game rules as presented.

Page 20

Children will follow game rules as presented.

Dear Family,

In Chapter 1 of **Mathematics Unlimited,** your child learns about addition and subtraction up to the number 12. One or more members of your family may want to do this activity with your child to reinforce skills learned in this chapter.

Materials
long sheet of paper
crayons

Project
Your child can make a personal time line. Draw a straight line across the length of the paper, about three quarters of the way from the top. Starting with the year of his or her birth, write every year until the present along the length of the paper. Draw a slash on the time line to show each year on the time line. Leave lots of space between each year. Let your child illustrate each year by drawing a picture of an important event that took place that year. Your child will remember some of the events, like the year he or she began school or the year a younger sibling was born. He or she may need help to imagine those earliest years.

Talk about the years. Start at one point and say, "Let's add 3 years. What happened then? Now let's go back in time and subtract 4 years from that year. What happened then?"

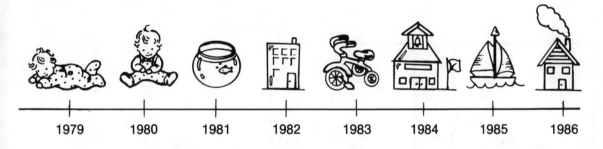

| 1979 | 1980 | 1981 | 1982 | 1983 | 1984 | 1985 | 1986 |

Dear Family,

In Chapter 2 of **Mathematics Unlimited,** your child learns how to use the greater than and less than symbols to compare two-digit numbers. One or more members of your family may want to do this activity with your child to reinforce skills learned in this chapter.

Materials
3 in. × 5 in. index cards
marker or crayon

Project
Write the numbers from 10 to 99 on index cards, one number per card. Shuffle the cards and place them face down on a table. Each family member should write the greater than symbol $\boxed{>}$ on one card and the less than symbol $\boxed{<}$ on another card.

Choose cards from the pile. Each family member takes a turn arranging the cards to make a number sentence using the greater than > or less than < symbol. For example, if the two cards selected are 16 and 24, the sentence would look like 16 < 24 or 24 > 16. If the number sentence is correct, that player keeps both cards. If the number sentence is not correct, return both cards to the bottom of the pile.

Continue until all of the cards have been used.

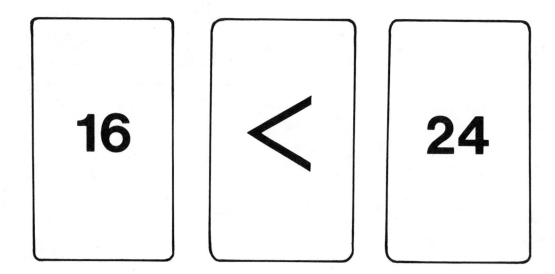

Dear Family,

In Chapter 3 of **Mathematics Unlimited,** your child learns how to find the sums of three one-digit numbers. One or more members of your family may want to do this activity with your child to reinforce skills learned in this chapter.

Materials
8½ in. × 11 in. sheet of paper
3 in. × 5 in. index cards
different-color pencils

Project
Have your child make a game board like the one below. It should have 16 squares in all. The number 18 should appear in the bottom row of boxes and in the boxes on the right side. The numbers 3, 2, and 1 should appear in the boxes as indicated.

Write each of the numbers from 1 to 12 on a 3 in. × 5 in. card, one number to a card. Shuffle the cards and place them facedown on the table.

Each family member chooses a color pencil. Participants take turns choosing cards and looking at the board to see if adding the number to one of the horizontal or vertical columns will make the sum of 18. Family members write the number they selected in a box in one of the rows on the game board using their color pencils.

When a family member adds the last number to the row (to make the sum 18), he or she circles 18 with the color pencil. Continue until all the 18's are circled.

This game can be played again by making another game board and changing the target number from 18 to 17, 16, or any other number!

		1	18
	2		18
3			18
18	18	18	

Dear Family,

In Chapter 4 of **Mathematics Unlimited,** your child learns about subtraction facts up to the number 18. One or more members of your family may want to do this activity with your child to reinforce skills learned in this chapter.

Materials
paper
pencils

Project
Have your whole family sit down together. Each person should write a list of things he or she would like to accomplish. Some ideas might be: make a card, write a thank-you note for a gift received, make a gift, finish a book, mend something, clean out a messy drawer, organize a collection, visit a neighbor, bathe the dog, give away outgrown clothes, call a relative who lives far away. Each person should try to write 15 to 18 items on his or her list.

Discuss the lists. Ask how many items are on each. Ask each person how many things they think they can do tomorrow. Ask how many things are then left to do. Continue asking questions that encourage subtracting one-digit numbers from the total items: How many things can you do in two days? in three? How many things are left?

Keep track of the lists each day and cross off items as accomplished. Ask the same kinds of questions.

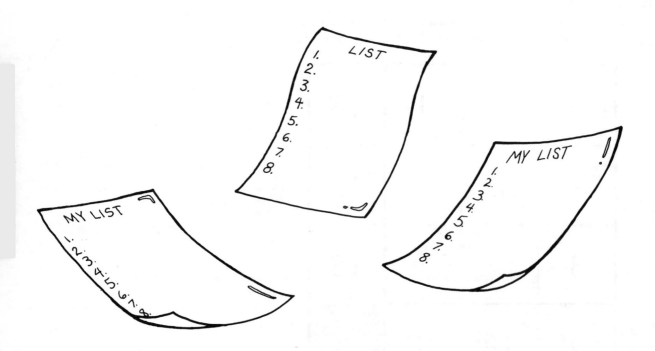

Dear Family,

In Chapter 5 of **Mathematics Unlimited,** your child learns about time, money, and metric measurement. One or more members of your family may want to do this activity with your child to reinforce skills learned in this chapter.

Materials
pencil
metric ruler

Project
Your family can do this project to record height differences of family members. Have your family members stand against the inside of a closet door or another place where you won't mind a few pencil marks denoting heights.

Have each person take turns standing up against the door as another person marks the person's height with a pencil. Label it with his or her name and the date. Using a metric ruler, measure each person's height and write it in centimeters next to the date. Your child may want to mark his or ner metric height once a month, say, on the first day of each month.

Have your child notice the differences from one month to the next. Who is taller? Does this change from month to month?

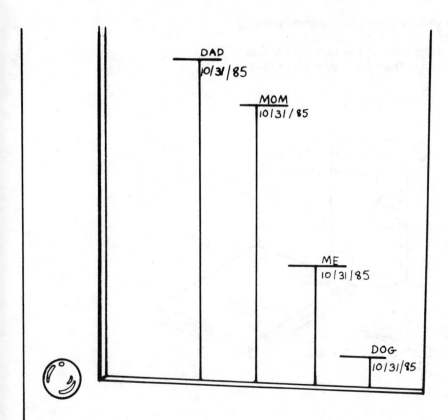

Dear Family,

In Chapter 6 of **Mathematics Unlimited,** your child learns about the addition of two-digit numbers. One or more members of your family may want to do this activity with your child to reinforce skills learned in this chapter.

Materials
masking tape
pen
scissors
small writing pad
play money
assorted items from around the house

Project
Your family can set up a store using empty shelves or a tabletop. Have family members collect small items from around the house. Or, each person can be in charge of making a few small items out of paper. Some ideas for things to make are: decorated note paper, cards, small books.

Cut small pieces of masking tape on which to write price tags for each item. Prices should range from 10¢ to 99¢. Your family might want to discuss how much each item should cost as they set up the store.

Each family member can take a turn at being the store owner, helping the customers pick out what they need. Customers can buy up to three items. The store owner adds up the cost of the items on a small pad and presents the bill to the customer. Then someone else takes a turn at being in charge.

Dear Family,

In Chapter 7 of **Mathematics Unlimited,** your child learns to subtract two-digit numbers. One or more members of your family may want to do this activity with your child to reinforce skills learned in this chapter.

Materials
lemon juice or white vinegar
thin white paper
toothpicks
100-watt bulb

Project
You can use invisible ink to write the answers to subtraction problems.

Have family members write out two-digit subtraction problems. Put each problem on a different sheet of paper. Use a toothpick dipped in lemon juice or vinegar to write the answers to the problems. After each answer dries, ask your child the answer to each problem. To check his or her response, have your child hold the paper over the lit 100-watt bulb. The answer will be revealed!

$$\begin{array}{r} 35 \\ -29 \\ \hline \end{array}$$

$$\begin{array}{r} 21 \\ -14 \\ \hline \end{array}$$

$$\begin{array}{r} 16 \\ -13 \\ \hline \end{array}$$

$$\begin{array}{r} 64 \\ -37 \\ \hline \end{array}$$

$$\begin{array}{r} 97 \\ -89 \\ \hline \end{array}$$

Dear Family,

In Chapter 8 of **Mathematics Unlimited,** your child learns about geometry and fractions. One or more members of your family may want to do this activity with your child to reinforce skills learned in this chapter.

Materials
food items for recipe below
mixing bowl

Project
Follow the recipe below to make 10 peanut butter balls:

2 tablespoons peanut butter
1½ teaspoons honey
¼ cup powdered milk
¼ cup crushed flakes of dry cereal

Mix peanut butter, honey, and powdered milk in a bowl. Use your fingers to blend well. Roll the mixture into balls the size of marbles. Roll the balls in the crushed cereal to coat them.

Count the 10 peanut butter balls. Have each family member take 1 ball. What fraction of the 10 is remaining? If each family member takes another ball, what fraction of 10 is left? Now if 1 family member puts 1 ball back, what would be the fraction of 10 that is remaining?

Dear Family,

In Chapter 9 of **Mathematics Unlimited,** your child learns how to find the perimeter and the area of different geometric figures. One or more members of your family may want to do this activity with your child to reinforce skills learned in this chapter.

Materials
red, blue, and yellow construction paper
12-inch rulers, one for each person
scissors
pencils
markers or crayons

Project
Cut six squares out of red construction paper. The measurements of the squares should be 1 in. × 1 in., 2 in. × 2 in., 3 in. × 3 in., 4 in. × 4 in., 5 in. × 5 in., and 6 in. × 6 in. Now cut the same size squares out of the blue and yellow construction paper.

Cut six rectangles out of red construction paper. The rectangles should measure 1 in. × 2 in., 2 in. × 3 in., 2 in. × 4 in., 3 in. × 4 in., 4 in. × 15 in., and 5 in. × 6 in. Not cut the same size rectangles out of blue and yellow construction paper.

On every red shape, label the length of the sides. On every blue shape, write the perimeter. Use a pencil and ruler to divide each yellow shape into square inches. Then use the marker to write the area.

Shuffle the red shapes and place them facedown on the table. Shuffle the blue shapes and place them facedown on the table. Finally, shuffle the yellow shapes and place them facedown on the table.

Taking turns, choose a red shape. Look at its dimensions. What is its perimeter? Without looking at the measurements, choose the blue shape with that perimeter. What is the area? Without looking at the measurements, choose the yellow shape with that area. Hold up the three shapes and see if they match. If they do, keep them. If they do not, return them to their places.

Continue until there are no shapes left on the table.

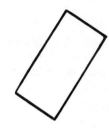
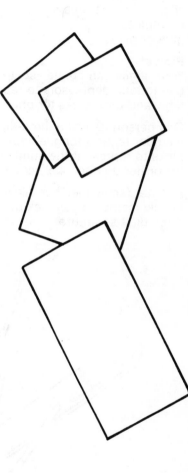
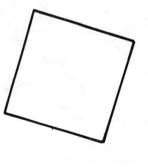
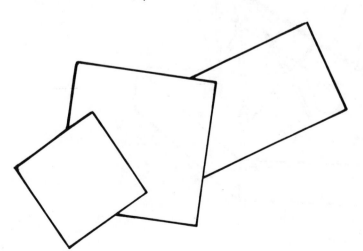

Dear Family,

In Chapter 10 of **Mathematics Unlimited,** your child learns about place values for numbers up to 999. One or more members of your family may want to do this activity with your child to reinforce skills learned in this chapter.

Materials
tongue depressors (available at hobby stores or drugstores)
sticks from ice cream pops
toothpicks
glue or paste

Project
Your family can create "sculptures" to represent three-digit numbers. Use tongue depressors to represent hundreds, ice cream sticks for tens, and toothpicks for ones.

One person names a three-digit number, such as 432. Each family member takes 4 tongue depressors, 3 ice cream sticks, and 2 toothpicks to represent the number, and glues the various sticks to make his or her unique "432 sculpture."

Another family member takes a turn naming a three-digit number. Family members can pick out the appropriate sticks to make another three-digit sculpture.

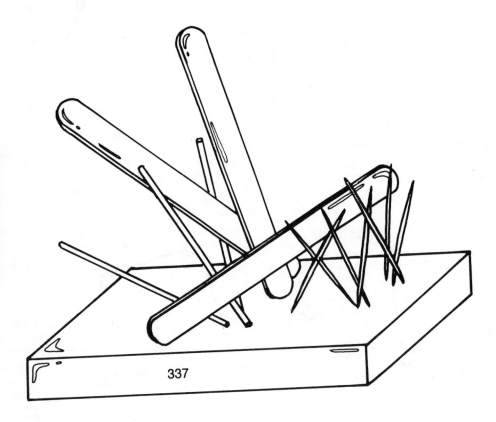

337

Dear Family,

In Chapter 11 of **Mathematics Unlimited,** your child learns about adding and subtracting three-digit numbers. One or more members of your family may want to do this activity with your child to reinforce skills learned in this chapter.

Materials
piece of cardboard at least 11 in. × 14 in.
strips of paper 1 in. × 14 in.
scissors
crayons

Project
Your child can make a counter to display three-digit numbers. The counter will have three sets of slits from left to right. Cut them with scissors. The slits will be in pairs, one inch above the other. The slits should be just slightly over 1 in. long. On each strip of paper, begin about 1 in. from the top and write the numbers from 0 to 9. Each number should be about 1 in. tall. Slide the strips into the slits so that only one number shows in each section. Your child now has a three-digit counter to decorate.

Set the counter by displaying a three-digit number. Have your child write down the number. Then move the counter to a different number. Have your child add or subtract the two numbers. Your child can then display the answer in the counter.

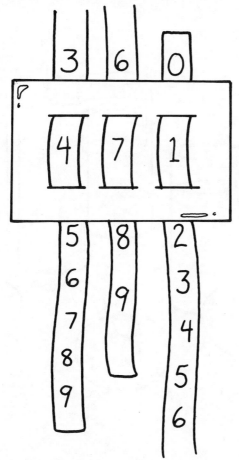

Dear Family,

In Chapter 12 of **Mathematics Unlimited,** your child learns about multiplication using factors up to 5 and gets ready for division. One or more members of your family may want to do this activity with your child to reinforce skills learned in this chapter.

Materials
pencil
paper
food, as needed

Project
Have your child plan a meal. He or she may want to have a lunch party. First, make a list of up to 5 people. Your child may want to invite 4 friends or just include family members. Then plan the menu, figuring out how much food to prepare. Here's an idea for a simple lunch for one child:

      cheese sandwiches (2 slices of bread, 1 slice of cheese)
      2 glasses of milk
      4 carrot sticks
      2 tomato slices
      1 apple

How much bread will be necessary for 5 guests? How many slices of cheese? Write out the foods and the amounts needed to feed the hungry guests. Your child may want to go beyond the planning stages and actually have a lunch party.

Table of Contents

9 +2	10 + 1	8 +4	3 +2	5 +4	4 +1
6 +6	3 +8	5 +6	4 +8	7 +2	10 + 2
5 +2	9 +3	3 +5	7 +4	5 +7	6 +4
4 +7	6 +2	8 +3	5 +5	3 +7	10 + 2
6 +3	9 +1	4 +6	3 +9	6 +5	8 +2
1 +7	4 +2	2 +7	5 +3	1 +6	7 +5

$$\begin{array}{r} 10 \\ -\ 9 \\ \hline \end{array} \qquad \begin{array}{r} 8 \\ -5 \\ \hline \end{array} \qquad \begin{array}{r} 12 \\ -\ 2 \\ \hline \end{array} \qquad \begin{array}{r} 11 \\ -\ 0 \\ \hline \end{array} \qquad \begin{array}{r} 8 \\ -6 \\ \hline \end{array} \qquad \begin{array}{r} 7 \\ -5 \\ \hline \end{array}$$

$$\begin{array}{r} 12 \\ -\ 7 \\ \hline \end{array} \qquad \begin{array}{r} 9 \\ -1 \\ \hline \end{array} \qquad \begin{array}{r} 11 \\ -\ 5 \\ \hline \end{array} \qquad \begin{array}{r} 11 \\ -\ 9 \\ \hline \end{array} \qquad \begin{array}{r} 9 \\ -4 \\ \hline \end{array} \qquad \begin{array}{r} 12 \\ -\ 1 \\ \hline \end{array}$$

$$\begin{array}{r} 6 \\ -0 \\ \hline \end{array} \qquad \begin{array}{r} 10 \\ -\ 7 \\ \hline \end{array} \qquad \begin{array}{r} 11 \\ -\ 3 \\ \hline \end{array} \qquad \begin{array}{r} 8 \\ -2 \\ \hline \end{array} \qquad \begin{array}{r} 11 \\ -\ 4 \\ \hline \end{array} \qquad \begin{array}{r} 9 \\ -6 \\ \hline \end{array}$$

$$\begin{array}{r} 11 \\ -\ 7 \\ \hline \end{array} \qquad \begin{array}{r} 11 \\ -\ 2 \\ \hline \end{array} \qquad \begin{array}{r} 12 \\ -\ 4 \\ \hline \end{array} \qquad \begin{array}{r} 12 \\ -\ 9 \\ \hline \end{array} \qquad \begin{array}{r} 10 \\ -\ 8 \\ \hline \end{array} \qquad \begin{array}{r} 11 \\ -\ 6 \\ \hline \end{array}$$

$$\begin{array}{r} 10 \\ -\ 4 \\ \hline \end{array} \qquad \begin{array}{r} 12 \\ -\ 6 \\ \hline \end{array} \qquad \begin{array}{r} 12 \\ -\ 5 \\ \hline \end{array} \qquad \begin{array}{r} 8 \\ -7 \\ \hline \end{array} \qquad \begin{array}{r} 12 \\ -\ 3 \\ \hline \end{array} \qquad \begin{array}{r} 6 \\ -4 \\ \hline \end{array}$$

$$\begin{array}{r} 11 \\ -\ 8 \\ \hline \end{array} \qquad \begin{array}{r} 10 \\ -\ 3 \\ \hline \end{array} \qquad \begin{array}{r} 7 \\ -3 \\ \hline \end{array} \qquad \begin{array}{r} 9 \\ -9 \\ \hline \end{array} \qquad \begin{array}{r} 12 \\ -\ 8 \\ \hline \end{array} \qquad \begin{array}{r} 9 \\ -7 \\ \hline \end{array}$$

tens	ones

tens	ones

tens	ones

tens	ones

tens	ones

tens	ones

tens	ones

tens	ones

tens	ones

tens	ones

tens	ones

tens	ones

1	2	3	4	5	6	7	8	9	10
11	12	13	14	15	16	17	18	19	20
21	22	23	24	25	26	27	28	29	30
31	32	33	34	35	36	37	38	39	40
41	42	43	44	45	46	47	48	49	50
51	52	53	54	55	56	57	58	59	60
61	62	63	64	65	66	67	68	69	70
71	72	73	74	75	76	77	78	79	80
81	82	83	84	85	86	87	88	89	90
91	92	93	94	95	96	97	98	99	100

Month _____

SUNDAY	MONDAY	TUESDAY	WEDNESDAY	THURSDAY	FRIDAY	SATURDAY

4 +7	7 +7	3 +9	9 +6	5 +8	8 +7
6 +7	8 +9	7 +5	5 +5	7 +9	9 +5
4 +8	6 +6	3 +8	7 +6	7 +3	8 +8
9 +9	6 +8	5 +9	4 +9	6 +5	8 +2
7 +6	9 +5	9 +3	8 +5	3 +7	9 +8
7 +2	1 +9	6 +4	9 +2	8 +3	9 +7

$$\begin{array}{r} 18 \\ -9 \\ \hline \end{array} \qquad \begin{array}{r} 17 \\ -8 \\ \hline \end{array} \qquad \begin{array}{r} 15 \\ -7 \\ \hline \end{array} \qquad \begin{array}{r} 17 \\ -9 \\ \hline \end{array} \qquad \begin{array}{r} 13 \\ -5 \\ \hline \end{array} \qquad \begin{array}{r} 14 \\ -7 \\ \hline \end{array}$$

$$\begin{array}{r} 12 \\ -7 \\ \hline \end{array} \qquad \begin{array}{r} 16 \\ -8 \\ \hline \end{array} \qquad \begin{array}{r} 14 \\ -9 \\ \hline \end{array} \qquad \begin{array}{r} 15 \\ -8 \\ \hline \end{array} \qquad \begin{array}{r} 11 \\ -9 \\ \hline \end{array} \qquad \begin{array}{r} 10 \\ -2 \\ \hline \end{array}$$

$$\begin{array}{r} 14 \\ -5 \\ \hline \end{array} \qquad \begin{array}{r} 16 \\ -9 \\ \hline \end{array} \qquad \begin{array}{r} 12 \\ -8 \\ \hline \end{array} \qquad \begin{array}{r} 13 \\ -4 \\ \hline \end{array} \qquad \begin{array}{r} 16 \\ -7 \\ \hline \end{array} \qquad \begin{array}{r} 13 \\ -7 \\ \hline \end{array}$$

$$\begin{array}{r} 15 \\ -6 \\ \hline \end{array} \qquad \begin{array}{r} 14 \\ -8 \\ \hline \end{array} \qquad \begin{array}{r} 10 \\ -1 \\ \hline \end{array} \qquad \begin{array}{r} 13 \\ -6 \\ \hline \end{array} \qquad \begin{array}{r} 15 \\ -9 \\ \hline \end{array} \qquad \begin{array}{r} 13 \\ -9 \\ \hline \end{array}$$

$$\begin{array}{r} 10 \\ -7 \\ \hline \end{array} \qquad \begin{array}{r} 14 \\ -6 \\ \hline \end{array} \qquad \begin{array}{r} 12 \\ -5 \\ \hline \end{array} \qquad \begin{array}{r} 11 \\ -3 \\ \hline \end{array} \qquad \begin{array}{r} 13 \\ -8 \\ \hline \end{array} \qquad \begin{array}{r} 10 \\ -5 \\ \hline \end{array}$$

$$\begin{array}{r} 11 \\ -4 \\ \hline \end{array} \qquad \begin{array}{r} 12 \\ -4 \\ \hline \end{array} \qquad \begin{array}{r} 10 \\ -6 \\ \hline \end{array} \qquad \begin{array}{r} 11 \\ -8 \\ \hline \end{array} \qquad \begin{array}{r} 11 \\ -7 \\ \hline \end{array} \qquad \begin{array}{r} 12 \\ -6 \\ \hline \end{array}$$

+	0	1	2	3	4	5	6	7	8	9
0										
1										
2							8			
3			5							
4										
5										
6										
7				11						
8										
9										

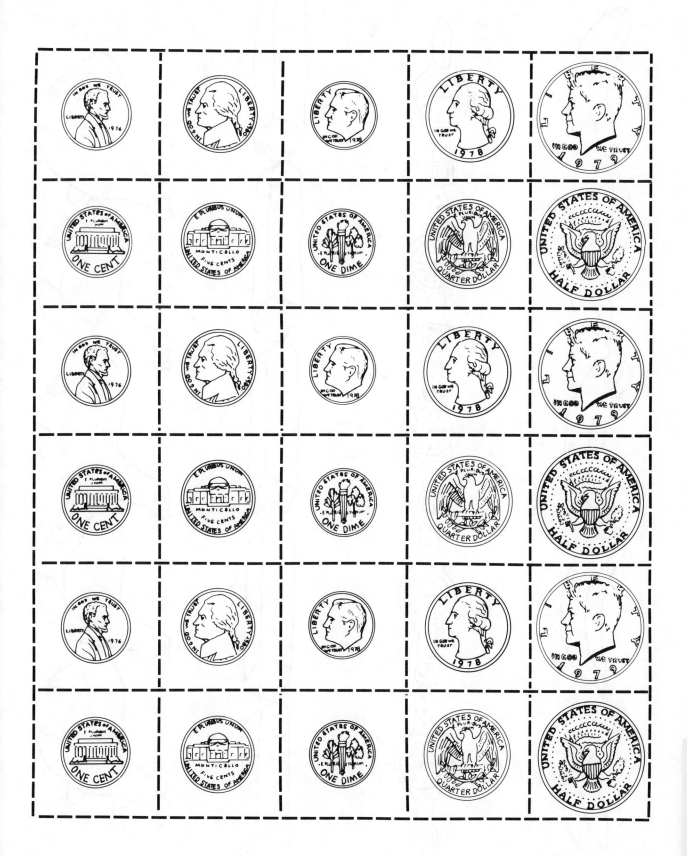

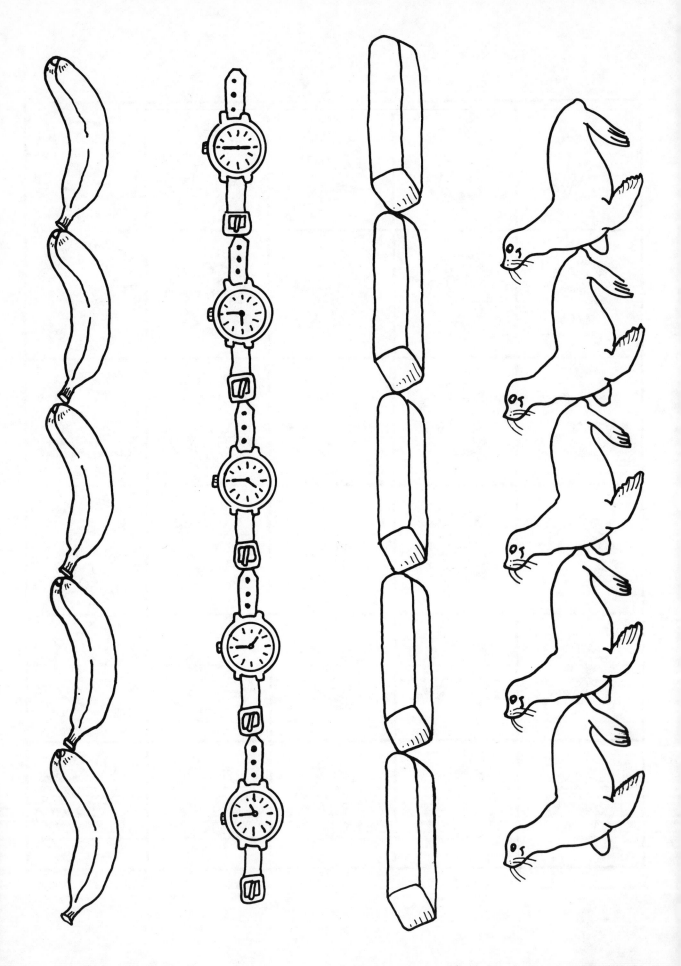

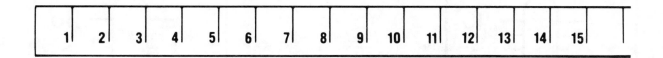

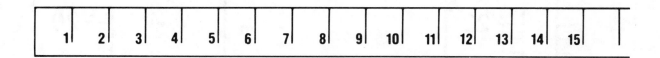

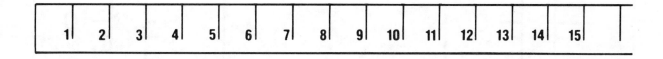

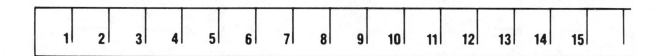

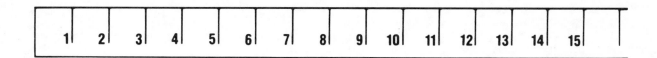

Centimeter Rulers

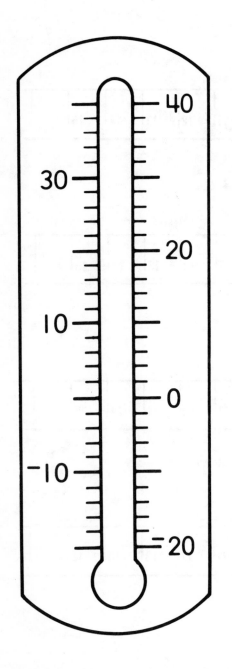

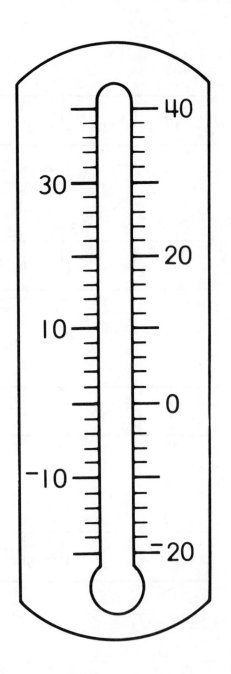

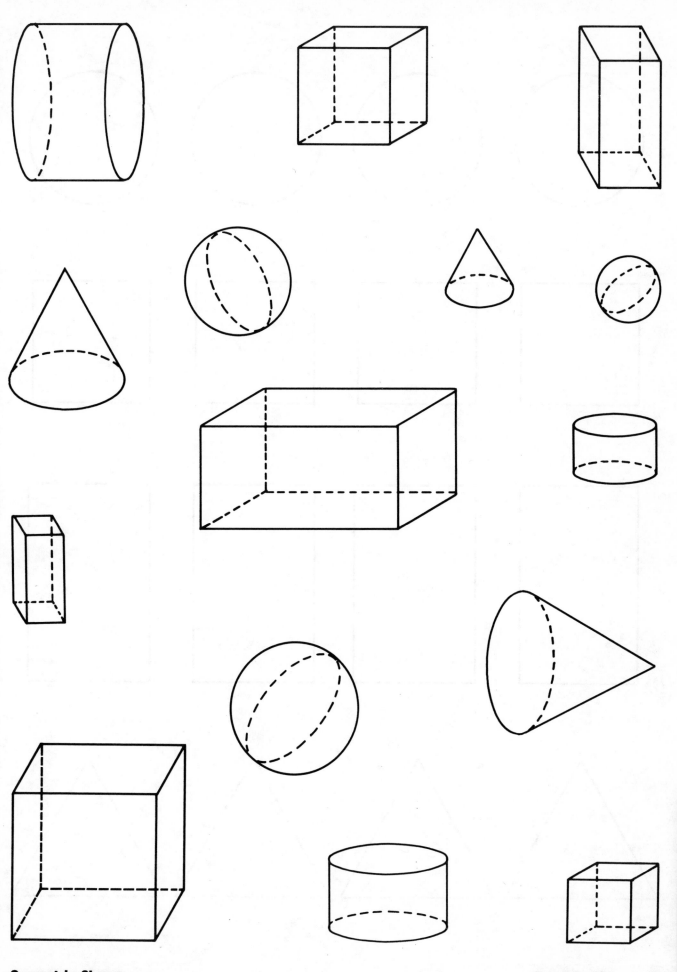

Geometric Shapes

Geometric Shapes

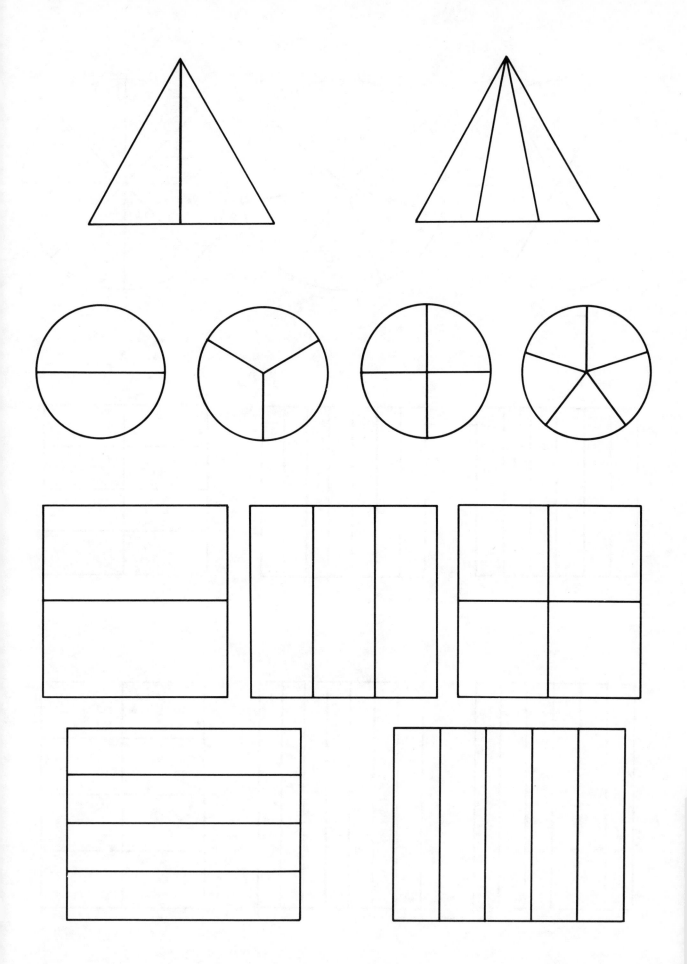

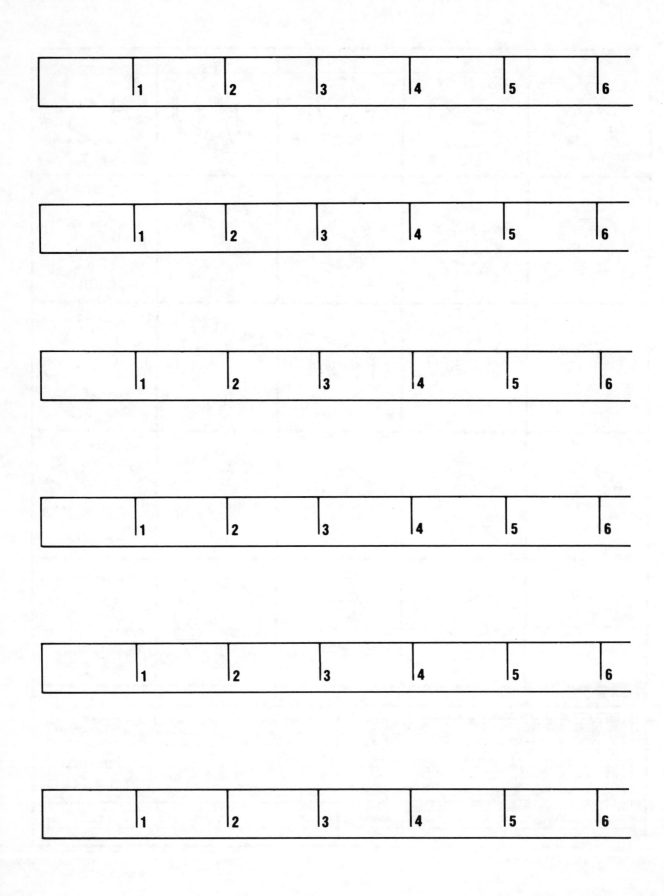

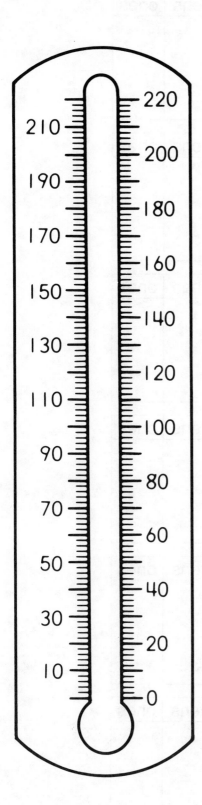

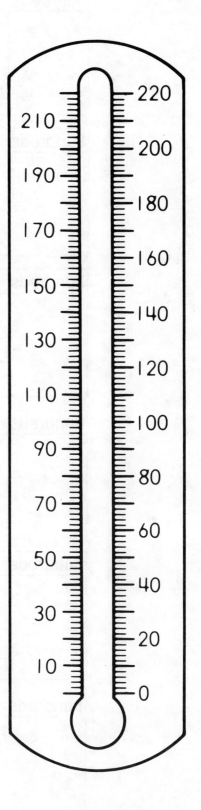

hundreds	tens	ones

hundreds	tens	ones

hundreds	tens	ones

hundreds	tens	ones

hundreds	tens	ones

hundreds	tens	ones

hundreds	tens	ones

hundreds	tens	ones

hundreds	tens	ones

hundreds	tens	ones

hundreds	tens	ones

hundreds	tens	ones

hundreds	tens	ones

hundreds	tens	ones

hundreds	tens	ones

hundreds	tens	ones

hundreds	tens	ones

hundreds	tens	ones

hundreds	tens	ones

hundreds	tens	ones

hundreds	tens	ones

hundreds	tens	ones

2 ×4	6 ×5	3 ×4	2 ×3	5 ×2	4 ×5
9 ×5	7 ×3	4 ×0	2 ×1	8 ×4	9 ×3
8 ×3	2 ×0	4 ×1	9 ×2	7 ×5	6 ×2
7 ×1	9 ×4	2 ×2	6 ×4	3 ×5	8 ×1
6 ×3	5 ×5	2 ×5	3 ×3	7 ×4	5 ×4
7 ×0	5 ×3	4 ×4	6 ×1	9 ×1	8 ×5

×	0	1	2	3	4	5
0						
1						
2						
3						
4				12		
5						
6						
7						
8						
9		9				

Multiplication Table

1-Inch Graph Paper

1-Centimeter Dot Paper

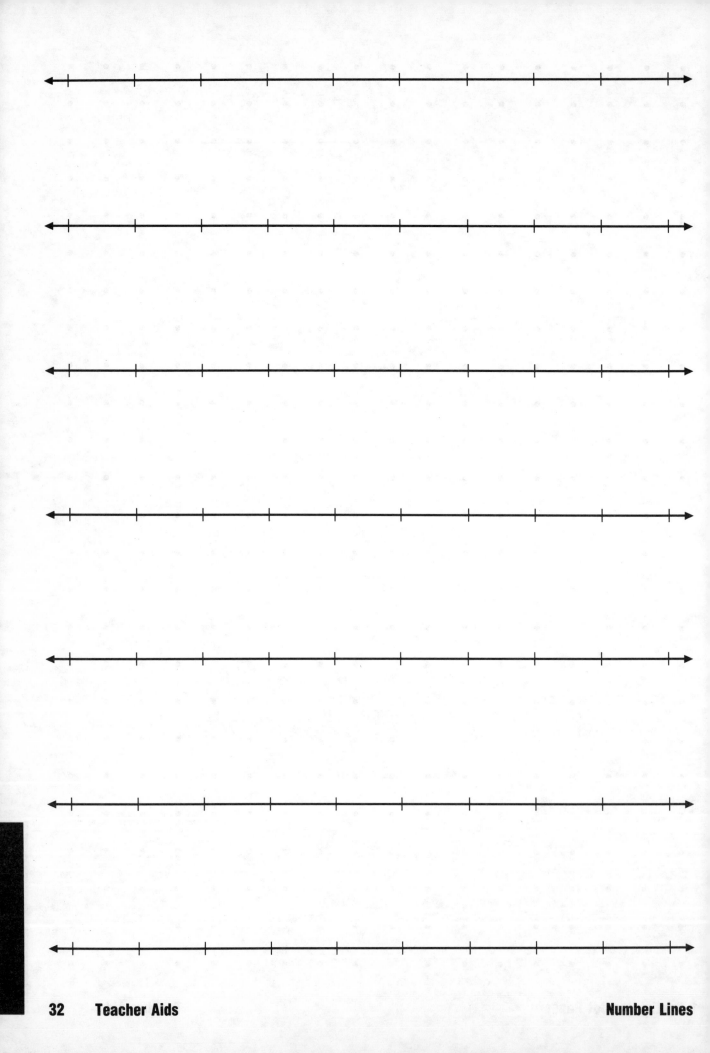